PSYCHIATRY, THE LAW AND MENTAL HEALTH

By

STANLEY PEARLSTEIN

1967

Oceana Publications, Inc.

Dobbs Ferry, New York

This is an entirely new book replacing Insanity Laws by W. R. Dittmar, the thirtieth in a series of LEGAL ALMANACS designed to bring you the law on various subjects in nontechnical language. These books do not take the place of your attorney's advice but they can introduce you to your legal rights and responsibilities.

KF
480
Z9
P4

Library of Congress Catalogue Card Number 67-16050
© Copyright 1967 by Oceana Publications, Inc.
Manufactured in the United States of America

TABLE OF CONTENTS

Page

Chapter 1   Introduction   1

Part I

PSYCHIATRY

Chapter 2   Psychiatric Therapies   4

    Curative Psychiatry   4
        Classical Psychoanalysis   4
        The Interpersonal School   7
        Cultural School   8
        Holistic School   9
        Individual Psychology   13
        Analytical Psychology   15
        Will Therapy   16
        Hypoanalysis   20
        The Psychotherapies   25
        Physical Therapies   28
        Psychosurgery   29

    Preventive Psychiatry   30

    Social Psychiatry   31

Chapter 3   Psychiatric Disorders   33

    Organic Disorders   33

    Functional Disorders   39
        The Psychoneuroses   39
        Functional Psychoses   44
        Personality Disorders   48
        Psychosomatic Medicine   49

    Conclusion   50

Part II

INSANITY: PROCEDURAL LAW

Chapter 4   Scope of Part II   52

    Definitions   55

Chapter 5   Care of Incompetents   57
    Home care   57
    Non-judicial commitments   58

	Voluntary commitment	58
	Involuntary commitments— Non-judicial	59
	Judicial commitments	62
	Release	65
	Writ of Habeas Corpus	66
	Constitutional Law	67
	Incompetent Veterans	69
	Perils of Incompetents	70
Chapter 6	Forensic Psychiatry	73

Part III

INSANITY: SUBSTANTIVE LAW

Chapter 7	Incompetents' Contracts	77
	Necessities	78
	Agency	79
	Negotiable Instruments	80
Chapter 8	Incompetents' Wrongful Acts	82
	Torts	82
	Crimes	84
	Intoxication	90
	Drugs	92
	Hypnotism	92
	Conclusion	93
Chapter 9	Other legal results of insanity	95
	Marriage and Divorce	95
	Property Rights	97
	Wills	97
	Gifts	98
	Deeds	99
	Bibliography	100
	Glossary	101
	Index	121
	Addendum to Index	123

Chapter 1

INTRODUCTION

This is a monograph on insanity as viewed and conceived by the disciplines of psychiatry and law. Insanity differs from sanity in degree and not in kind. Some place on a theoretical line from zero (sanity) to one hundred (insanity) psychiatry, law and other disciplines of the social sciences place a mark, saying in effect, on this side is sanity and on this other side insanity. It must always be kept in mind that there is not a sudden change but a gradual almost imperceptible one. Most important, the different disciplines will disagree as to where this mark is to be placed for any single person and even within the same discipline, the mark may differ depending on the question asked. Thus in law, a person may have sufficient mental ability to make a valid will, that is, be pronounced sane, and at the same time, not have sufficient mental ability to have the necessary criminal intent to commit a crime, that is, be pronounced insane.

As Justice Holmes once wrote:

> There is no doubt that in many cases a man may be insane, and yet perfectly capable of taking the precautions, and of being influenced by the motives, which the circumstances demand. But if insanity of a pronounced type exists, manifestly incapacitating the sufferer from complying with the rule which he has broken, good sense would require it to be admitted as an excuse. 1/

Definitions are of course of the utmost importance, and to simplify matters, the three elements of this book will be defined at this point. Unfortunately, the word insanity has no technical meaning either in law or medicine, and it is used by judges and legislatures indiscriminately to convey either of two meanings: (1) any type or degree of mental defect or disease; (2) such a degree of mental defect or disease as to entail legal consequences, e.g. as to require commitment to a mental hospital, the appointment of a committee or guardian or to avoid a contract or relieve from responsibility from crime. 2/ Hereinafter, the first meaning will be used in this popular sense of referring to the as yet undetermined mental status of an individual. Where this has been determined, more precise psychiatric and medical terminology will be used.

Psychiatry is the simplest element to be defined. It is merely that branch of medicine concerned with the study, recognition and treatment of disorders of the mind.3/ The alert reader will at once be curious or question whether this definition includes organic disorders of the mind. Strictly speaking from the point of view of medicine, it does not but since this is a book on the psychiatric and legal juxtaposition of insanity, it must cover both types of mental disorder. Actually, the medical specialty of neurology covers most organic mental diseases, although its exact definition is the branch of medicine concerned with the structure and organic functioning of the nervous system. An example of the interrelation of these two medical specialties will suffice. In order to qualify in the specialty of psychiatry, a doctor must not only pass the special boards on psychiatry but also several selected boards in neurology. This latter however does not qualify him as a neurologist. If he passes both sets of full boards, he becomes a neuropsychiatrist.

In order to define the third element, law, it is necessary to make a preliminary diversion into the field of political philosophy. Any community, i.e., a group of two or more people which has an actual or implied agreement or understanding by which peace and order are maintained is a polity. This is deliberately made broad enough to cover the situation of two castaways on a desert island to the complicated legal-economic-social structure of an entity like the United States of America.

Law then is the means by which an entity maintains peace and order internally, which is its polity. It is tripartite in organization consisting of making (legislative), interpreting (judical) and enforcing (executive). Any polity's legal system is always of this threefold nature even though one or two of these parts may seem to be absent as in the case of a dictatorship or the system inaugurated by the great law-givers of the world such as Moses, Solon, Lycurgus, Hammurabi or Mohammed.

Since this book concerns itself with Anglo-American law or the common law, a further complication ensues because the common law is inductive, reasoning from the particular to the general, introduced into Western thinking or philosophy by Francis Bacon, as opposed to legal systems based on Roman Law which is deductive, reasoning from the general to the particular. Thus in Anglo-American non-statutory law, we are confronted with a series of judicial decisions or precedents each defining insanity **for the purposes of that particular case.** From these individual cases, general principles can be induced (in popular parlance we generally use the words infer or deduce despite the fact that in logic they are diametrically opposed) from which theoretically a new situation or legal case can be determined.

But actually, no case is identical with a previous one or else there would be no need for litigation (justiciation) and we are left with a series of cases which should point in one particular direction, but often instead point in almost every direction of the compass. So while the term law as used herein has been accurately defined, when we come to determine the law as applied to a particular situation in which the decision turns on a definition of insanity, we find ourselves wallowing in a mass of verbiage. Shakespeare, not unacquainted with the law, gives to Hamlet, his most eloquent hero at his oratorical zenith the following reply to Polonius' query as to what he is reading, "Words, words, words." It is a pithy, laconic epitomization of Anglo-American law's greatest defect.

Footnotes

1/O.W. Holmes, Jr. "The Common Law," 1881 ed., p. 109.
2/Hinsie & Campbell, Psychiatric Dictionary, page 387B.
3/Compare the more detailed and psychoanalytically-oriented definition from Webster's Unabridged Dictionary, 3rd ed., contained in the Appendix.

3

Part I—PSYCHIATRY

Chapter 2

PSYCHIATRIC THERAPIES

Let us emphasize again that this book is not about insanity and psychiatry and law, a combination of elements in the sense of physics, but about psychiatry and law as they fuse on the subject of insanity, a new molecule chemically speaking. This is usually called forensic psychiatry which is defined by Dr. Winfred Overholser as "the application of psychiatric knowledge and techniques to legal procedures."[1]/ Psychiatry itself is a relatively new medical specialty and the word itself came into general usage only about fifty years ago.[2]/ Previously a specialist in mental illnesses was often called an alienist, and up to about forty years ago, the latter word was used more specifically to mean a forensic psychiatrist.

While psychiatric therapies are not properly a part of this book, they are dwelt on in this chapter at great length because of the importance to the intelligent layman in understanding the fusion of psychiatry and law above referred to. Also, as the reader will come to see, they complement the discussion of psychiatric disorders contained in Chapter 3.

The three portions of psychiatry covered here are curative psychiatry, preventive psychiatry and social psychiatry.

Curative Psychiatry
Classical Psychoanalysis

Psychoanalysis is probably the most important of the curative therapies since its invention by Freud (with Breuer) in 1893 made his reputation as one of the Titans of medicine, leading the Second Psychiatric Revolution as Zilboorg phrases it,[3]/ and its preeminence over all other curative therapies though the eclectic therapies have been making inroads on its one time near-monopoly.

Hinsie and Campbell's Psychiatric Dictionary defines psychoanalysis, paraphrased as follows: The separation or resolution of the psyche into its constituent elements. The term has three separate meanings: (1) Freud's procedure for investigating mental processes by means of free association, dream interpretation and interpretation of resistance and transference manifestations; (2) a theory of psychology developed by Freud out of his clinical experience with hysterical patients; and (3) a form of psychiatric treatment developed by Freud which uses the psychoanalytic procedure (definition 1 above) and which is based on psychoanalytic psychology (definition 2 above). Freud considered the cornerstones of psychoanalysis theory to be: the assumption of unconscious mental processes, recognition of sexuality (and aggressivity), and the Oedipal complex. Ernest Jones has delineated seven major principles of Freud's psychiatry:

1. Determinism—psychical processes are not a chance occurence.

2. Affective processes have a certain autonomy and can be detached and displaced.

3. Mental processes are dynamic and tend constantly to discharge the energy associated with them.

4. Repression.

5. Intrapsychic conflict.

6. Infantile mental processes—the wishes of later life are important only as they ally themselves with those of childhood.

7. Psychosexual trends are present in childhood.

Many people think of it as synonymous with Freudianism since it is the monument of its founder's work in medical psychology[4] and his well deserved claim to fame.[5] Essentially it is a depth psychology, using free association and the couch so that the therapist can be an unobserved observer and working on Freud's structural hypothesis of a tripartite mental apparatus denoted by him respectively as the id, the instinctual reservoir of man having its basis in the anatomy and physiology of the human being and which is in the unconscious, operates on the pleasure principle, seeks immediate discharge and is not concerned with reality or consequences; the ego, the control apparatus of the psychic structure, responsible for perception, thinking, memory and judgment, controlling the gateway to motility (spontaneous motion), organizing and synthesizing, functioning on all three levels of conscious, preconscious and subconscious, characterized among other things by words, ideas, logic, order and a sense of time and operating at the conscious and preconscious levels on the reality principle, e.g. postponing a present pleasure in favor of a later, greater pleasure; and the superego, the latest to develop of the psychic structure, arising out of the ego at the time of the resolution of the Oedipus complex, containing the rewarding and punishing values of the parents, having the ego-ideal and conscience as different aspects and operating on all three levels but mainly on the unconscious.

All neurotic phenomena are the result of an insufficiency of the ego's normal function of control, either because the stimuli which the ego is asked to handle are too much or because it is too depleted in energy to handle the ordinary stimuli. A neurotic conflict, caused by the damming up of the instinctual tensions and the overwhelming of the ego, is structurally a conflict between the id and the ego, with the superego participating in a number of ways. In order to be a neurotic conflict, one aspect of it must be unconscious. The external world of reality also influences any neurotic conflict.

Classical psychoanalytic therapy's aim can be stated in a number of ways. Ultimately, it aims to resolve the infantile neurosis which is the nucleus of the adult neurosis, and thus do away with neurotic conflicts. From the ego's standpoint, it intends to make possible the ego's confrontation with the id, superego and the external world, so that these three agencies of psychic life will not force it to irrational and inappropriate acts and defenses. It seeks to make the unconscious conscious, to overcome the infantile amnesia so that the hitherto forbidden instinctual strivings and memories are made conscious. It aims to redistribute psychic energies so that the ego has more energy at its disposal once it is freed from the burden of maintaining

6

previous defenses thought to be necessary. Finally, psychoanalytic therapy differs from others in that it strives for structural, i.e. permanent changes in the relationships among the id, ego, superego and the external world.

There are several other concepts of Freud's to be mentioned in order to understand fully his classical psychoanalysis. Resistance refers to all the conscious and unconscious impulses, emotions, activities and motives of the patient which oppose the therapies aims to establish a rational ego. Defense is quite similar to resistance but refers only to the ego's conscious and unconscious operations. Transference is all the feelings that the patient experiences toward the analyst which are displaced from figures in his past. These feelings are intense, inappropriate, changeable, infantile and ambivalent. All psychotherapies are in part based on transference reactions, but psychoanalysis is the only one based on systematic interpretation of transference phenomena.

There are several systems of psychotherapy which, while not Freudian in the classical sense just described, are so close to Freud's and deriving so much from his writings, teachings and theories as to be called variants of psychoanalysis or quasi-Freudian systems. Among these are the therapies connected with the names of Harry Stack Sullivan, Erich Fromm, Karen Horney, Alfred Adler, Carl Jung, Otto Rank and Lewis R. Wolberg.

The Interpersonal School

This covers Harry Stack Sullivan's contribution to the theories and techniques of psychotherapy and properly is one of the psychoanalytic therapies. Among man's basic drives, called "satisfactions" are his need for sleep, rest, shelter, food, drink and lust satisfactions, and these can be appeased only in interaction with others. An adult can satisfy these needs largely by himself, and thus Sullivan's thesis seems faulty. But Sullivan takes a dynamic view of man's life, and in the case of a newborn infant, it is obvious that man is dependent on others to satisfy his needs, originally his parents. And as he grows up and his needs and environments change, he similarly attempts to satisfy his needs with others, arriving at security, tension or some intermediate stage depending on his success. Putting aside Freud's structural concept of id, ego and superego, Sullivan emphasizes the one-ness of the person and the interdependence of all.

Cultural School

Fromm's work is usually called by this name and is also one of the psychoanalytic schools. He is more in the tradition of philosophy and sociology than the others considered here. He pictures man in relation to his culture and his attempts to fit in with it or to change it. He sees living as two types of relation to the outside world: acquiring and assimilating things, and relating to people. The orientation by which an individual relates himself to the world, partially or completely, forms the core of his character. In character types, Fromm lists the non-productive (or neurotic) and the productive (or healthy). The non-productive consists of the following types: the receptive orientation is typified by the person who feels that all that is good or necessary is outside himself, who needs love yet cannot give love, who looks for answers to others but makes no effort to get them himself and who looks for "miracles." He tends to optimism but tends to anxiety when the outside source of help seems to be dwindling. The exploitative orientation has the same premise as the receptive orientation, i.e. the source of all good is external to the individual. He takes what he can by cunning and action, and is pessimistic, suspicious and angry. The hoarding orientation believes an individual's security depends on what he can save or own. He attempts to possess others rather than love them. He is obsessively rigid and obstinate. The marketing orientation is peculiar to our times and comes into being in a highly organized capitalistic society such as America's. Success as a commodity is the only measurement and personal qualities have no value. Social mobility and the constant breaking and reacquiring of social ties leads to isolation, loneliness and a feeling of hopelessness and despair.

The productive character on the other hand is he who is able to use his powers and realize his potentialities. He is free and not dependent on someone who controls his powers. He is at one with himself, well integrated and an individual.

Fromm's aim is not merely to have the patient learn to adjust to his culture, but to have him realize his potentiality and individuality which may transcend his own culture.

Holistic School

Karen Horney's school of psychotherapy is called holistic, holism being defined as the concept that all aspects of living must be studied as a single entity. The study of the parts cannot explain the whole, because the latter is something different from the summation of its parts. There are several sciences **relating to** the person but none **of** the person. Physiology, psychology and sociology deal with artifically separated single aspects of the human organism, but there is no single science at present that studies the human person in its totality. The holistic viewpoint takes a stand diametrically opposed to Euclid; it insists that the whole is greater than the sum of its parts.

Together with Harry Stack Sullivan's interpersonal approach, Karen Horney's school represents the two chief branches within the "dynamic-cultural" school of psychoanalysis. Horney never explicitly formulated her methodology which was empirical, descriptive and intuitive, inductive and pragmatic and her primary interest was therapy. Theory was derived from therapy. It is growth oriented; it shows that much that previously was considered restricted by the individual's constitution merely represents a block which can be lifted or removed. Like Fromm's, it is an optimistic philosophy. She denies Freud's theory that man is by nature sinful or ridden by primitive instincts, which if true, cannot be relinquished by anyone. Hers is a morality of evolution wherein man progresses to a higher and higher level of morality of self and group by an ever increasing awareness and understanding of self.

Since her theories were never fully developed and she is, in effect, a disciple of Heraclitus, the classical Greek philosopher whose theories are based on Becoming, not Being, it is easiest to study Horneyism by studying her four major books in order of appearance: "The Neurotic Personality of Our Time," 1937; "New Ways in Psychoanalysis," 1939; "Self-Analysis," 1942; and "Neurosis and Human Growth," 1950.

In the first, she develops and describes the neurotic person who lives among us, their many similarities and the effect of different cultures on the persons affected. Neuroses are generated as well by cultures as by individual experiences. Sociology comes into the picture to join with psychology in understanding and curing the neurotic person. Horney emphasized the complexity of cultures and the individual reactions to, with and against the norms established by them, whereas to Freud, culture was the mass product of individual biological drives.

While still remaining within the general fold of psycho-analysis, Horney aired her differences with Freud in her second major book, "New Ways In Psychoanalysis." She approved his doctrines of strict determinism of psychic processes, the determination of actions and feelings by un-conscious motivations and that the latter, which drive us, are emotional forces. She agreed with his concept of re-pression, his emphasis on the meaningfulness of dreams, that neuroses arise out of conflicts, that neurotic anxiety plays a crucial role in neurosis, and that child experiences play an important role in neurotic development. However, all these ideas were formulated in ways differing from Freud's. Finally, she emphasized Freud's furnishing the methodological tools of therapy: the concepts of resistance 6/ and transference and the free association method.

But Horney did differ with Freud's biological orientation and the genetic, mechanistic, dualistic, evolutionist nature of his thinking. As did many before and after her, Horney severely criticized Freud's libido theory, feeling that unwar-ranted analogies and generalizations were poor evidence, that the validity of data concerning erogenic zones was highly dubitable, that it gave a distorted perspective on human relationships, that it attempted to explain the whole

10

from the part and that it limited therapeutic possibilities.

Freud regarded narcissism as instinctually derived, arising from the libido, which being of limited quantity, furnishes less for the narcissist to give to others as love since he expends so much more on self. He assumed normal self-esteem and self aggrandizement to be narcissistic phenomena, differing only quantitatively from the neurotic. Horney, taking a more cultural viewpoint, looked upon narcissism as self-inflation, not self-love with a need not for love but for admiration from others. A narcissist, being alienated from himself, actually cannot love self or others. Narcissistic trends arise frequently, not because rooted in biology, but because our culture produces and places value on them. Fears and hostilities are stimulated and spontaneity curtailed by imposed standardization. Striving for prestige is a culturally prescribed method of overcoming fears and inner emptiness. Freud's philosophy, "The goal of life is death" naturally conflicted with one that held the goal of life is living, and inspiring human hopes of changing and growing.

In actual treatment, Horney valued Freud's discovery that one could use therapeutically the patient's emotional reactions to the analyst (transference) but rejected the idea that these were reactive infantile feelings. She criticizes this as leaving out of account the patient's actual character. Freud's suggestion that the analyst be like a mirror restricts his spontaneity according to Horney. Instead she postulates an analyst who functions as a whole person, using his personal analysis, self analysis and therapeutic efforts to help his patient. Freud's ego was considered by Horney to be a neurotic phenomenon which was not inherent in human nature. It was caused by the squelching of the spontaneous self, leading to an alienation from self. Her therapy aimed at restoring the patient's spontaneity, his faculty of judgment, his spiritual self.

In Horney's third book, "Self-Analysis" she discusses the feasibility, desirability, types and limitations of self-analysis. She contends that the focal point in the whole neurotic structure is what she calls neurotic trends, which are the attempted solutions to early psychic disturbances which in turn become the source for further disturbances.

These early disturbances cause the basic anxiety which is characteristic of all neurotics and consists in feeling helpless and alone in a potentially hostile world. To cope with this, the child develops neurotic character trends. When moving **towards** people, he accepts his own helplessness, yet tries to win their affection and to lean on them. When moving **against** people, he takes hostility for granted, yet determines, consciously or unconsciously, to fight. When moving **away from** people, he wants neither to belong nor fight, but to keep apart. In each attitude, one of the elements involved in the basic anxiety is overemphasized: helplessness in the first, hostility in the second and isolation in the third. For a normal person, there is no reason why these three attitudes should be mutually exclusive. Each can be used in its proper function, they can be mingled or fused as the occasion demands and by complementing each other, a harmonious and integrated whole can be achieved. But in the case of a neurotic, this cannot happen since neurotic trends are compulsive, indiscriminate and contradictory. And what started within the family extends to all relationships in life, ultimately invading the entire personality and this conflict born of incompatible attitudes constitutes the core of neurosis and is best denominated basic.

Using these basic concepts of Horney which are developed exhaustively in this book, a neurotic during an interruption in analytic treatment or after completion may help himself further to develop a more healthy personality, but Horney warns that it is a radical way and a hard way but not impossible.

Horney's fourth and final book, "Neurosis and Human Growth," is an epitomization of all her previous work and a summary of her theories and concepts. She begins on a high philosophical note defining, in the context of a "Morality of Evolution," man's essential nature which she sees as good, constantly striving onwards and upwards toward self-realization, which every individual seeks unless deprived of a chance to grow. Life is dynamic, never being, always becoming as it strives to achieve the self-realization of each person's ambition, growing and rising if the struggle progresses successfully, diminishing and sinking if this ambition is frustrated giving rise to neurotic conflicts and gradually destroying the entire personality unless psychoanalytic therapy is able to reverse this trend. This part of Horney's theories was derived from Adler as we shall see when we come to study him.

Since neurosis is a process involving disturbances in more and more areas of the personality, Horney defines the goal of therapy not as symptom removal or "cure"—because a neurotic process cannot be "cured"—but as helping the individual outgrow his neurotic difficulties and asserting his development to assume a more constructive direction.

It is rather ironical that Horney's concept of a dynamic and everchanging psychoanalytic theory and technique prevented her from formalizing her theses in a book, since it is as impossible to contain constantly changing ideas in a book as it is to contain the essence of a great river in a hand held cupful of its water.

Horney's work, theories and techniques have been delineated at such great length because they have had a tremendous effect on younger therapists in this country, and because, in describing them, we ineluctibly elucidate further the theories of Freud himself of whom Horney was a sincere if sometimes critical disciple.

Individual Psychology

This is the term applied to the school of Alfred Adler, the first of three great disciples to break away from Freud. He was the most intransigently holistic of these three and retained the least of his early Freudian training and practice.

Adler himself described his system as follows: "By starting with the assumption of the unity of the individual, an attempt is made to obtain a picture of this unified personality regarded as a variant of individual life manifestations and forms of expression. The individual traits are then compared with one another, brought into a common plane, and finally fused together to form a composite portrait that is, in turn, individualized." He dismissed all of Freud's meticulous biological study of infantile sexuality.

He posits a universal inferiority in every person caused by the feeling of infantile helplessness, which every one strives to overcome. The "family constellation" meaning the family around him on whom he depends is of great importance in the infant's solution of the inferiority and other problems facing him. Adler even went as far as individualizing the problems of siblings in accordance with the order of their birth. The creation of solutions to these problems, which under unfavorable conditions are erroneous, leads to neurosis. As the mistaken solutions are relied on, the neurotic tends to set his fantasy goals higher and more rigid. The occurrence of minor real gratifications and moderate real achievements then becomes meaningless. This part of Adler's philosophy was highly valued by Karen Horney and was incorporated into her system.

Adler's therapy is based on a strong therapist-patient relationship, depending upon the patient's own understanding of the mistakes in his life style. The therapist must understand the individualistic pattern of the patient's strivings so accurately, that his comments and observations will strike home. This relationship is the means of bringing the patient to significant insights and self-knowledge. The therapist is alert to prevent the patient gaining control of the treatment and tries to establish himself as co-worker rather than the powerful benign doctor of Freud's powerful transference. The Adlerian is more inclined to offer constructive suggestions on new ventures as the patient begins the "real life" that therapy envisions.

Today, Adlerism has only a small following in America yet it has the richness and imaginativeness of the early adventures in the field of psychoanalysis and contains many concepts still valuable today, as instanced in Horney's adoption of one of them. In a field in which dissection, analysis and fragmentation are so necessary to reach the roots of the difficulties besetting the mental patient, it is not amiss to rename Adler's Individual Psychology as Psycho-Synthesis.

Analytical Psychology

This term is used to denominate the school established by Carl Gustav Jung, Freud's second great disciple to break away from him. It diminishes the role of sexuality in mental and emotional disorders. Jung regards the mind as something much more than the sum total of past experiences. It is also a preparation for the future with aims and goals that it tries to realize within itself. The reminiscences of personal experiences become unconscious and join with fundamental ideas and trends of all mankind (the "collective unconscious") which act as the background of all human thought and emotion. Jung stresses a mystical, religious factor in his concept of the unconscious.

Jung's influence in the areas of art, literature and history has been continuous and profound, although his influence upon psychology fell soon after the 20's but is on the rise today. He distinguished between a personal unconscious not unlike Freud's and what he called the "collective unconscious." He discovered that schizophrenics, of varying backgrounds, had remarkably similar appearance of images which were similar to some aspects of the dream process in normal and neurotic persons and to the great myths, legends and art forms observable all over the world. This suggested that the mind of man as well as his body bears traces of his racial past; that he is predisposed to certain deep expectations, longings and terrors rooted in prehistory over and above his experiences as an individual. These representatives of the collective unconscious are few in number and called archetypes by Jung. The main outlines of these types are universal in nature but the representational details vary with the individual's personal and cultural background.

The collective unconscious must be considered in relation to the personal unconscious and conscious control. In psychosis, the archetypes appear because the ego is overwhelmed. At this point, Jung's theories, very similar to Freud's in many respects, enter into a complex system with many new concepts and ideas which must be minutely described and fitted into the Jungian formula, a task much too profound and space consuming to be contained in a book of this type. The inquisitive reader can be referred to the works of Jung himself or to Ruth Munroe's book referred to in the bibliography, which while excellent in itself is difficult to understand on the subject of Jung without reference to his own writings.

Jung's therapy aims at better integration of the personality. The unconscious is made conscious but in a different sense from the Freudian sense of release from repression. The neglected functions of the personality which have entered the unconscious and become shrivelled and monstrous must be restored to ego-consciousness in the interest of harmonious integration which is approximated in normal living. Dream interpretation is a major tool but free association in the Freudian sense is not a Jungian technique.

Will Therapy

This phrase denotes the form of psychotherapy developed by Otto Rank, the third of Freud's early disciples to break away from him. He was not a doctor, but his native brilliance plus his background in the physical sciences, in art, history and philosophy made him a welcome member of Freud's early coterie.

Rank's theory, also referred to as the birth trauma, is based on his belief that the separation of the child from the mother at the moment of birth is the central element of neurosis. It is believed to lead to two sets of strivings: 1. To return to the womb or 2. To re-enact separation and achieve independence. In therapy, separation reactions are studied as well as the struggle of will manifested in the patient's desire to continue therapy (and dependence) or to stop it (and become independent). The patient is actively encouraged to assert himself so as to develop and strengthen his will.

The post natal psychosexual crises of childhood are variations on the theme of the issue from the womb terror and the wish to return to embryonic bliss. The painful birth experience leaves all of us with some **primal anxiety.** The universal desire to forget this pain is called primal repression.

The mother's ministrations help the infant to reknit a sense of unity with his environment, but this is again broken by the process of weaning.

Rank interprets dreams and other unconscious phenomena as symbolic representations of the womb, birth canal, etc. Like Adler and Jung, there is an element of the holistic in Rank in his rejection of Freud's concept of man as merely a battleground of warring instincts and his insistence that man could, indeed must, be understood in terms of his direction as a whole person, by an emphasis on the person's **will.** There is a sort of polarity in Rank's concept of the person. On the one hand, there is the need to break away, to be one's self, individual and independent which is the very essence of life. On the other, there is the longing for the effortless bliss of the womb, the need to be one with one's surrounding world, which longing is essentially death.

As the infant grows older, he begins to sense the potentialities of his own independent personality through the development of a **counterwill,** a will directed against the parents. This, like the hostility of a patient in treatment, is highly constructive but it does lead to the development of guilt. If this counterwill is treated intelligently by the parent, is accepted as well as the independence of which it is a manifestation, while at the same time gently asserting the adult's own independence, there is no development of a life fear and consequent inhibition of further free growth but a harmonious integration of the growing child with his environment.

However, with imperfect families living in an imperfect society, there is always some imperfection and thus swings of the pendulum in the individual's psychologic make-up between the life urge and the death wish described above. Rank's view of the ideal is not a straight upward going line, but a series of new problems between the individual and his environment (usually exemplified in terms of persons) successfully solved by new integrations on a constantly broadening basis as the child's horizons expand into those of an adult.

Rank terms the ideal personality an **artist,** not in the

17

strict sense, but denoting any person, even an average or neurotic one, who has successfully ridden the growing wave of his expanding relationship between self and other (or the world) and who has successfully resolved the polarity between the life fear and the death fear. In his necessary emphasis on the moderate man, of course Rank is hearing as have so many others the thunderous and all pervading voice of the great Stagyrite, Aristotle, who was said to be moderate to the point of excess.

Rank uses two other terms to categorize people which were used above in describing the artist: average and neurotic. The former makes a commonplace adjustment to the universal problems facing all mankind. He is generally socially useful, but not very estimable. His main problem of separation has been solved by him by an unthinking identification with the conventions of his community, and his measure of value is proportionate to the measure of those conventions' value. He is not valuable intrinsically. In times of upheaval and revolution, he tends to become prey or predator. He is the personification of the unspectacular failure so dramatically brought to life in the character of Willy Loman in Arthur Miller's "Death of a Salesman."

Rank's neurotic is a far more interesting person since he is the frustrated artist, in Rank's definition of the latter, a universal figure of pathos and tragicomedy found in all forms of art in all ages. He at least has managed to achieve a true separation beyond the average man's cheap solution of specification with the group mores. He has not been able to achieve the creative integration of trends that is the hallmark of an artist. His pendulum swings too widely. Though he had achieved separation, it is laden with guilt. He tends to react totalistically (or to over-react) without keeping matters in proportion or partialization which is learned by reality judgments successively integrated at different dynamic levels, as the healthy child copes with successive crises of his life from weaning onward. The artist's experience and learning from reality factors modify his interpretation of people and events meaningfully, as an expert surfer manipulates his body and board to cope successfully with the changing conditions of the ocean. The neurotic's interpretation, if it can be called that, is generalized in terms of his own needs and is inflexible, being incapable of change to meet changing needs. Even his separation is mainly hostile, still imbedded in the counterwill and guilt-ridden.

Rank's therapy then emphasizes strongly the reliving of the past and the correction of former errors and divigations, as do all the psychoanalytic schools to a greater or lesser degree. The therapist tries to help the neurotic to accept his separateness without guilt and gladly accepts resistance as a valid expression of the will. Even hostility is a desirable manifestation of the separate self of the neurotic, to be understood and "loved" as such.

The transference is the keynote of Rankian therapy and its aim is not through release or catharsis, or even insight as differently defined by Freud, Adler and Jung, but through the experience of acceptance as one's true, separated though guilt-laden, self. But the therapist must beware of giving or appearing to give too much "love" and of too great a totalistic reaction without sufficient correction from valid reality judgments. Meaningful partialization (or viewing events in proportion) oriented towards "reality" must be developed by the therapist and learned by the patient.

As the patient talks about current and past experiences, especially as he approaches the termination of the treatment, the therapist must watch the transference and its mood, most urgently when the patient begins to act upon his newly acquired feelings and tends to become bogged down in difficulties. Here, the therapist, in his turn the surfer, must disentangle himself from his transitory role as substitute father or whoever and accept whatever role is thrust upon him as in the early Freudian concept of the transfer, switching when necessary to realistic supporter or critic, without permitting the patient to damage the fundamental treatment relationship.

Rank's ideas, once we surmount his early overemphasis on the birth trauma, are of tremendous value, and permeate the ideas and techniques of the later Freudians and eclectics.

19

Unfortunately however, he has no organized psychiatric following at present, but he has had a profound and continuous influence in the field of social work.

Hypnoanalysis

This variation of Freudian psychoanalysis is also called hypnotherapy, since its emphasis is on therapy rather than theory and is usually associated with the name of Lewis R. Wolberg, M.D. Hypnoanalysis can be best defined as the use of hypnosis in psychoanalytic therapy (classical or any of its variants) as an aid to removing resistances (or blockages) that prevent awareness of unconscious material. Regression and revivification under hypnosis may open up pathways to memories which are not available to the patient at the adult waking level. However, no matter what material is elicited in the trance stage, in order to be effective it must be integrated and incorporated into the more conscious layers of the psyche.

Hypnotism is one of the most ancient of psychic agencies, arising in superstition and fed by the fear and awesome veneration it engendered in the multitudes. Its dubious origins, its seemingly miraculous results and its attraction to it of misguided healers, quacks and mountebanks has created an aura of disrepute and obloquy which has compromised and weakened its reputation to this day.

Hypynosis has been falsely claimed as a scalpel to the unconscious to effect a short cut psychoanalysis, as a means of destroying symptoms and as a device to conform the patient to philosophical precepts and modes of living exemplified by the therapist. The doctor or medical psychologist who is interested in hypnosis and studies it goes through three phases: 1. Over-confidence, generated by a few early successes which cause him to view the potential of hypnosis awesomely; 2. Skepticism, caused by later failures and disappointments such as short lived improvements or incorporation into the patient's neurotic frame-work his hypnotic experiences which neutralize trance suggestions and increase and bolster his defenses against therapy; and 3. Integration and balanced judgment as the successes and failures balance out and the therapist learns to view hypnosis meaningfully and realistically.

To date there is no theory sufficiently comprehensive to explain the complex manifestations of hypnosis. However, we are easily able to observe and classify these manifestations.

In every hypnotic trance, there can be observed many different kinds of phenomena, constantly fluctuating with psycho-physiological changes within the individual and the meaning to him of the hypnotic relationship. Some of these trance elements can be utilized for therapeutic purposes. These therapeutically useful manifestations will now be discussed.

First, there is a remarkable easing of tension as muscles progressively relax. Continued stress may damage both physiological and psychological body functions, creating somatic imbalance, obstructing the healing process in physical disorders and exaggerating the symptoms of psychological illnesses. Any device to alleviate tensions can neutralize these distructive forces, and create conditions for the effective operation of spontaneous and applied curative forces. Chronic and progressive ailments can also be helped.

Hypnosis has successfully helped a wide variety of medical, orthopedic and neurological ailments in which stress plays a destructive role including hypertension, Raynaud's disease, coronary disorders, paroxysmal tachycardia, cerebral accidents, asthma, enuresis, impotence, chronic gastritis, dyspepsia, spastic and ulcerative colitis, dysmennhorrhea, amenhorrea, menhorragia, tabes, Parkinson's disease, syringomyelia, muscular dystrophy, multiple sclerosis and Sydenham's chorea.

Second, the patient under hypnosis develops an extraordinary suggestibility to pronouncements from the hypnotist which are not too anxiety provoking. The degree of enhanced suggestibility in a particular subject is of greater importance than the depth of the trance, since hypnosis wields its effects largely through the influence of suggestion. The negative effects of suggestion can be seen in voodoo illnesses and even deaths, and similar occurrences in superstitious tribes. The positive effects of suggestion can be used in numerous ways.

One researcher has proved that hypnotic and posthypnotic suggestions may produce at statistically significant levels of confidence the following effects: 1. An increase in psycho-motor speed and endurance and a decrease in physical fatique; 2. An increase in the span and duration of attention; 3. An increase in the speed of learning; 4. An increase in the speed of association, mental alertness, concentration and general mental efficiency; 5. An improvement in the application of abstract abilities in relation to number content; 6. An improvement in the speed of reading comprehension; and 7. A heightened sense of enjoyment in performance. Suggestions may even be able to break conditioned reflexes, thus altering set habits.

Hypnosis, by appropriate suggestions, may serve as a powerful motivational determinant. Sick patients may be motivated to execute medical orders, which they had previously resisted. Obese persons may be aided in following and keeping on fat reducing diets. Cardiac convalescents can be helped to avoid excessive strain and overactivity, yet maintain the desired, therapeutic amount of activity during their convalescence. Numerous other ailments, both major and transient, can be aided by means of suggestion skillfully implanted in the subject's mind by a skilled hypnotherapist.

Proper suggestions can lower or eliminate overt and subjective responses to painful stimuli which, together with reduction of tension, promotion of muscle relaxation and raising the threshold of pain, produce an analgesia. This may be therapeutically utilized in minor surgical procedures, diagnostic exploration, obstetrics and dental operations. The latter usage in fact has given rise to a dental-anaesthesia specialty called hypnodontics. This has been employed: 1. To quiet a terrified and tense patient so that he will permit exploration and corrective dental measures; 2. To reinforce local anaesthesia by lowering the required dosages and helping to overcome gagging, coughing and excessive salivation; 3. To foster better co-operation in using dental appliances; and 4. To correct habits that interfere with dental health, such as nail biting and unconscious teeth grinding and gnashing.

Hypnoalgesia in the field of childbirth can be very effective. During the long period when pain relieving measures are required, chemical anaesthetics may have an enormous toxic potential for both mother and child. When administered in the second stage of childbirth, they may depress uterine contractions and impair the respirations of the child. It is obvious that hypnosis can be of great assistance to the orthodox anaesthias in helping the mother through her birth ordeal. In fact, the so-called "natural childbirth" method, which consists of a prior conditioning of the patient in proper breathing and relaxation during childbirth, is probably a form of hypnosis.

Hypnoanalgesia can also be valuable in controlling organic and functional pain. In the former, the patient is comforted by helping him to detach from his suffering. The pain stimulus is not eliminated as it may be in functional disorders, but, by focusing the patient's interest away from himself, his distress can be ameliorated. This hypnosuggestive relief is very similar to occurrences in real life where events conspire to produce a situation where the individual so focuses his attention away from himself that he achieves a quasi-hypnotic trance. Examples are soldiers, severely wounded, who have felt no pain in the heat of battle; athletes oblivious to extensive physical injuries in an athletic contest, so obsessed are they by their all pervading urge to win; religious martyrs, capable of enduring unbelievable torture, so transposed are they by the all-enclosing horizons of their ecstacy.

Diagnostic uses of hypnosis are based on the heightened suggestibility that it creates. Sometimes it is necessary to distinguish certain organic from functional disorders. Occasionally, a patient in a deep state of hysteria will report physical symptoms that would require immediate surgery.[7] Here the prudent surgeon will call for psychiatric consultation and in the immediacy of the situation, the psychiatrist will find the tool of hypnosis of great value in calming

23

and quieting the patient and determining whether the pain is organic or functional.

However, the hypnoanalyst must beware of using strong authoritative suggestions with a patient whose symptoms serve an important purpose in maintaining psychological equilibrium, since the chances of success in creating a heightened suggestibility are remote, and this failure may cloud and inhibit other attempts at making hypnotic and post-hypnotic suggestions. But as already indicated, the heightened suggestibility created by hypnosis is of tremendous potential value when properly used almost to the point of sensationalism.

Third, there is a lifting of repressive controls as the trance deepens. There is a relative withdrawal of attention from the outside world and a refocussing on the inner self and its processes. Certain aspects of the patients's unconscious life that have eluded him in the waking state enter the realm of his awareness. The lifting of repression releases charged emotional components, fantasies flourish and primitive mental operations with more vivid symbolization become activated. These tendencies can be used in psychoanalytic therapy by encouraging emotional catharsis, by bringing the patient into closer contact with repressed needs and conflicts and by aiding a search for significant memories toward exploration of genetic determinants. But hypnosis is still only a psychoanalytic tool, and where there is no extraordinary resistance or no insurmountable block to the exploring of the unconscious, hypnosis is not necessary.

Fourth, the development of a unique relationship between operator and patient, a sort of mobilization of transference, which reassures the patient, assuages his sense of helplessness and anxiety and can be used as a sort of short cut which can be used by the operator in getting through to the patient more quickly. This phenomenon, when it occurs, is not single and entire in itself, but when used in the course of psychoanalytic therapy as an additional tool, can be very effective in overcoming blocks, coping with the more difficult problems that arise and in general, smoothing and easing the course and shortening the time of the therapy.

24

This subject of hypnosis has been delineated at great length because of the great popular interest in it, its constant and long time appearance in literary works of all types and its importance to the subject of insanity, especially criminal. We are not so much concerned here with the melodramatic picture of a man of evil wreaking vengeance on an enemy by hypnotizing a young and innocent victim to perform his evil deed for him, a picture more from fiction than fact. Rather we are interested in quasi-hypnotic situations where a highly suggestible person can be unwittingly influenced by a dominant figure to perform an act, criminal or otherwise, which is, strictly speaking, not of his own volition. A highly suggestible person may have such a psychic structure as to mobilize his own actions by a sort of auto-hypnosis. Are the crimes, torts, contracts and other legal relationships of such a person governed by some of the rules governing those of an incompetent?

The Psychotherapies

These are approaches to the problems of mental illness and attempts to explain and solve them, not directly connected with Freud's theories and disciples, but sometimes arising out of reaction to them. Generally, they apply solely to psychoses, unlike the psychoanalytic therapies which cope with lesser disturbances as well. They will be briefly noted.

Psychobiology is the study of the biology of the mind including its anatomy, physiology and pathology. It is generally connected with the name of Adolf Meyer. It conceives of the mind as the integration of the whole-functions of the total personality and that man is the indivisible unit of study, which can be approached from several different levels. Ideal mental health is the maximal ability of, plus the best opportunity, for, getting along with people without the interference of inner conflicts. Psychobiology is a genetic-dynamic science which studies personality development in the light of its environment. Its central theme is "mind in action" and its aim is to integrate the patient with his environment.

Organismic psychotherapy is a theory of therapy developed by T. Burrow also denominated phyloanalysis or phylobiology which will shortly be explained. It is a complex system grounded in biology which emphasizes the individual as a whole organism and contrasts it with the experience of the race.

The prefix phylo is derived from the Greek word phylon meaning race, tribe, clan, people or nation, but it is difficult to define in its combining form of phylo. The latter is best understood in the word phylogenesis, which is a biological term meaning the genealogical history and evolutionary development of a species as distinguished from the ontogenetic (the individual's development) development of the individual. Haeckel's biogenetic law states the "phylogeny is always recapitulated by ontogeny." This means that as the embryo develops in the womb, it goes through, in miniature, all the stages of evolution.

Burrow's method of therapy attempts to make the patient aware of the divergences between his behavior patterns which depart from those of the ideals of the individual and the group. Phylobiology is a behavioral science that posits a biological unity as a central governing principal motivating the behavior of the organism as an individual and as a species. Its connection with Jung and his theories is obvious.

Existential psychiatry is a bastard product of existential philosophy and psychoanalysis. It has the character of a pure rather than an applied science. It pictures the individual in existential terms weighted down by the alienation, anxiety, guilt and other emotional and spiritual problems of modern man in a godless world. It thinks of his existence in the term of being, but this is to be understood in a dynamic rather than static sense. Therapy aims at making the patient aware of his own existence in this world of tremendous problems leading eventually to death and to learn to live and cope with it positively by bringing out the best in him. It is a very modern and ad hoc concept of people's problems, but as yet, it is still in the stage of evolving into a complete and finished process with integrated theories and techniques.

Group therapy is a means of aiding several persons suffering different but similar emotional illnesses by treating them together under the supervision of one psychotherapist. Generally speaking, the back and forth discussing of individual therapy is replaced by a group discussion initiated, directed and supervised by the therapist. Since persons constantly find themselves participating in groups of different types throughout their lives, their membership and activity in an artificial, selected, harmonious, supervised group is believed to be of great help to them in dealing with their emotional (or functional mental) problems. Depending on the preferences and the school of psychiatric thought of the individual therapist, he attempts to restore lost self-confidence to his patients, stimulate their pathologic, self defeating attitudes so as to externalize them to the point where the individual patient can recognize their absurdity, make them verbalize so that they can talk freely and intelligently about their own as well as others' problems and create an atmosphere where old and new methods of thinking and acting can be practiced and experimented with. Group therapy has sprung into great popularity since World War II and is still in a state of flux, but it appears to be another valuable therapeutic tool in the battle against mental illness.

Psychodrama may be said to have evolved from the failures of group therapy and the rebellion of the repressed actor in the patient against the word or literalism. It goes beyond psychoanalysis as does group therapy and emphasizes non-verbal and symbolical actions in place of the talk of the verbally oriented psychotherapist.

It usually occurs in a group but may be restricted to one patient only. It is a spontaneous acting out of the emotional problems of the patient with the aim of achieving a catharsis. While still a psychotherapeutic tool, it differs from other therapies in the following ways:

1. The production put on by the patient (or patients where group therapy is also practiced) is the sole frame of reference for observation and guidance;

27

2. Attention is focused on the present, not the past;

3. Free association (no matter how differently defined by different schools) is replaced by free acting and interacting, which includes free association of words; and

4. The two dimensional couch is replaced by a three dimensional social space or stage-like substitute.

Physical Therapies

Insulin shock therapy introduced by Sakel around 1932 is the first of modern shock treatments. It is considered the most acceptable somatic treatment for schizophrenia and is used almost exclusively as a physiological treatment of that disease. It consists in the production of coma, with or without convulsions, through the intramuscular administration of insulin. It results in improvement in the patient and the lessening of the effects of his schizophrenia. Precisely how the therapy works to effect its results is still not entirely known, but the psychiatric profession accepts it on an empirical basis.

Convulsive shock treatment is another physical therapy used in the treatment of schizophrenia. It was based on the belief that schizophrenia and epilepsy usually do not occur together and therefore may be antagonistic towards each other, and several known cases of schizophrenia which temporarily disappeared after a spontaneous convulsion. The convulsion was first produced by pharmacologic means, that is, the intramuscular injection of various drugs. Later, pharmaceologic inhalants were used. Shock from a strong electric current was still later used to produce the convulsion. Its results with schizophrenics are similar to those where insulin is used. However, it achieved spectacular results in the treatment of the affective psychoses such as depression, where it achieved almost 100% recoveries during the period of its use, although future bouts of depression cannot be prevented.

Drug therapy has been an integral part of psychiatry since its inception. Few have causal influence, but by controlling symptoms, they make the patient more comfortable and therefore more amenable to those forms of psychotherapy which require the cooperation of the patient. These drugs are mostly sedatives (tranquilizers) or stimulants. However, there are at present so many of these on the market either under generic or trade names that it is impossible to cover them all. Also, there probably is no field of medicine in which the individual nature of the patient and his physio-psychochemical make-up are so important. Here, the drug and dosage must be tailor made to the needs of the patient. Generalization under these circumstances is virtually impossible.

There are several miscellaneous physical therapies whose names practically describe their techniques. There is carbon dioxide therapy where inhalation of this gas, alone or mixed with oxygen, has been used to ameliorate the condition of mental patients. Continuous sleep treatment is a method of artifically prolonging sleep over a long period which is claimed to be helpful in catatonic excitement states of schizophrenia, in all phases of manic depressive psychoses but especially those not responding to electric shock, in subacute anxiety states and generally whenever a major degree of anxiety is part of the clinical picture. Narcoanalysis is a part of psychiatry which used the injection of drugs, usually sodium pentothal, the so-called "truth drug," to induce a sleep during which psychiatric treatment and diagnosis can be performed. The word narcosynthesis is used to denote the particular technique of intensive psychotherapy of acute war neuroses, and panic and anxiety states which helps to effect a rapid cure of neurotic and psychotic manifestations caused by the war, enabling the psychically wounded to return in short order.

Hydrotherapy is still another form of physical therapy.

Psychosurgery

Finally, the art of the surgeon has been mobilized in the never ending struggle to conquer or at least ameliorate the dire consequences of mental illness. Psychosurgery is a general term now used to describe any form of brain operation performed to relieve mental illness or intractable pain, but with the usual paradoxy endemic to the medical profession, the surgeon who performs such operations is called, not a psychosurgeon, but a neurosurgeon.

Among the methods of surgery are scalpel such as trephining, ultrasonic devices, and miscellaneous cutting tools; and non-cutting procedures such as chemical coagulation and electric current. This depends on the choice of the individual neurosurgeon.

Generally speaking, psychosurgery is used as a last resort, but it has achieved some very cogent results.

Preventive Psychiatry

This category can be broken down into two sections: mental hygiene and psychiatry in the medical schools. It is not too germane to the subject of this book but it is well to notice it briefly to round out the complete psychiatric picture.

Mental hygiene or mental health as it is also called is in a state of evolution as are most other fields of specialization related to psychiatry. At present, it contains four main subdivisions.

The first, the prevention of mental diseases can be exemplified by the cure of mental illnesses caused by infectious diseases by the use of sulfonamides and antibiotics and paresis by penicillin.

The second, the publicizing of psychiatric problems and the methods of dealing with them is not properly speaking a function of psychiatry, whose prime purpose is the treatment of patients, not publicizing its facilities. But in a democratic form of government, the facts and theories about psychiatry and its role in promoting, preserving and restoring mental health must be made known to the public. This is done by general educational efforts and the sponsorship of organizations publicly or privately supported, for the purpose of helping those with mental health problems.

The third, the promotion of mental health in the population, while similar in some respects to the second, differs in a more direct application to specific situations. Thus all through a person's life, from pre-natal advice to his mother, child guidance programs, career guidance advice, psychiatric help when needed and rehabilitation of a damaged personality, it is sought to give him the optimal state of health at various developmental levels.

The fourth, the application of a philosophy of public health to psychiatry is not easy to define. Basically, its underlying thought is the changing and evolving of the concept of a "welfare state" from the "rugged individualism" of early depression days. It means the application of research and clinical data for the prevention of disease and the promotion of health for the entire population by such organization as are adaptable to, or required by, the culture of the population concerned. In recent years, the former narrow definition of health as anatomical and physiological intactness of the body has been expanded from this negative concept of absence of disease to the positive concept of complete, physical, mental and social well being.

Psychiatry in the medical schools has achieved a higher status and increased prestige in recent years to the point where it occupies 10% of the curriculum in some medical schools. A new generation of doctors, who in effect served their internships and residencies on the battlefields of World War II and Korea, became interested in psychiatry by the demands of war and readjustment to peace.

Today, most departments of psychiatry attempt to teach general medical psychologic data and more specific psychiatric data as part of the general training of the future physician. The three year graduate psychiatric training programs of intership and residency is best provided by a psychiatry department that is an integral part of a medical school and its affiliated hospitals and clinics. Here the future psychiatrist meets a wealth of patients of all types, providing him with tremendous opportunities for research and training.

It is obvious that these increasingly psychiatry-oriented medical schools and post graduate training centers are an integral part of preventive psychiatry and publicizing of the needs for, and resources of, mental health.

Social Psychiatry

In psychiatry, this is the emphasis placed on the environmental influences and the impact of the social group on the individual. This emphasis is made not only with regard to etiology, but also for purposes of treatment and, more importantly, in preventive work.

In the study of Sullivan's interpersonal relationship theory and the therapies of group psychotherapy and psychodrama, we have seen specific instances of heightened emphasis on the relationship between the individual and his environment. Implicit in all theories and therapies is the idea of reaction and interaction by the patient with members of his immediate family and later groups. This sociological element, always present in any psychiatric situation, has been given more and greater emphasis, as psychiatry has enlarged its surroundings, to the point that it has now become under the above subheading, an important and valuable branch of the theoretical or pure sicience aspect of psychiatry. And in group therapy and psychodrama, it has become an important therapeutical tool as well.

Footnotes

1/American Handbook of Psychiatry, p. 1887.
2/Ibid at p. 1888. The discrepancy in figures is due to the different publication dates of that book and the instant one.
3/Zilboorg, Gregory, A history of medical psychology, Chap. II, p. 486.
4/Zilboorg's phrase as exhibited in the title of his book, supra note 3.
5/This latter part is a reworking of Dr. Ralph P. Greenson's essay "The Classic Psychoanalytic Approach" in The American Handbook of Psychiatry, Chapter 69 at p. 1400ff.
6/However, Horney uses the concept "blockage" in place of "resistance" as dynamic rather than mechanistic and placing less of an onus on the patient. Cf. Blockage in Glossary.
7/This is a fairly common experience for even a non-hysterical patient who has suffered a series of renal colic attacks caused by kidney stones. He has had so many bouts of severe pain, that he often reports to his urologist's office prepared for immediate surgery only to be told that x-rays indicate that the stones are quiescent and incapable of causing any pain, let alone a colic.

Chapter 3

PSYCHIATRIC DISORDERS

This chapter will cover not only all psychiatric disorders but all peripheral disorders and related sciences and disciplines. This is necessary because the clinical picture presented to the forensic psychiatrist (by pretrial examination or examination at the trial) may indicate several other conditions besides that degree of incompetency necessary to affect legal decisions, and just as he as the expert must be familiar with the entire field, so it must be delineated for the general reader.

Organic Disorders

We begin with organic disorders affecting the mind, that is, where there is a measureable or otherwise apprehensible change in the organs and physical structure of the putative incompetent. Prior to the advent of penicillin, one of the highest percentage of new admissions to mental hospitals was due to syphilis-caused general paralysis or paresis. The clinical picture presents a gradual breakdown of the mental and physical personality of the patient, leading to death unless cured. The principal mental symptom is dementia around which varying psychologic and neurologic manifestations are grouped. There are several laboratory methods that reveal the presence of the disease such as optical examination, electroencephalogram, spinal tap, etc. Before the discovery of penicillin, salvarsan, bismuth and mercury were tried in the late 19th century but without success. Malaria therapy or the artifical creation of a high fever, developed over a period roughly from 1877 to 1917, achieved a 35% recovery rate. Penicillin when it was applied in the fight against syphilis was literally "a wonder drug." It was highly efficacious (one study showed a 90% recovery),

33

practically without risk, inexpensive, of short duration, causes the disappearance of mental symptoms soon after treatment has begun and the successfully penicillin treated patient becomes a well adjusted individual without the need of psychotherapy. Truly, penicillin has made syphilis and its physical and mental effects of little more than historical interest, though unfortunately enough cases of untreated or unsuccessfully treated patients remain so that the subject must continue to be studied.

The next subject is that of senility, where there have been organic changes. This is another tremendously important subject and steadily growing, because of the larger percentage of "aged" persons in the entire population caused by the medical revolution since World War II in other medical fields which has conquered or reduced the inroads on middle-aged people, extending their life expectancies and bringing them into the field of possibility senility. All tables and statistics concerning the over-65 population and their percentage in mental hospitals have been growing from decade to decade and almost from year to year.

Structural damage of the nervous system is often but not necessarily present with mental diseases of old age. Aging, or senescence, alone does not create senility, since the latter implies a pathological condition, that is, aging plus precipitating factors. Chronological age is unimportant; it is biological or physiological age that counts. Mental symptoms of senility are disturbances of memory and orientation and a state of confusion. Psychological tests such as the Rorschach have been used to measure the amount of mental deterioration. Physical symptoms are lessened perceptions, thinning, skin wrinkling, wasting of muscles, tremors and changes in posture and walk. This is a psychosocial problem because aging people feel let down, no longer needed, unwanted in the working force and neglected as a has-been. Correcting these problems helps considerably. Finally, there is no direct correlation between cerebral pathological findings and the development of mental symptoms. Apparently these develop according to an individual's heredity or family history, psychic pressures in the course of his life, recent severe illnesses, traumatic shocks and other things which medical science are gradually learning. The relatively new medical specialty of gerontology studies the phsyical and mental effects of aging and, short of achieving immortality, is making great strides in extending life expectancies in meaningful and productive years and making them as pleasant and pain free as possible.

Alzheimer's and Pick's diseasee are so called presenile psychoses because they occur in the so-called presenilium, a period roughly from age 45 to age 65. The former is very similar to senile dementia and is often called a severe and early variety thereof. The latter is a degenerative disease, usually fatal, affecting both mind and body and classified with the former only because it generally occurs during the same pre-senium period.

A cerebral arteriosclerosis induced psychosis is just what its name implies, a state of mental illness caused by hardening of the arteries of the brain. Not every case of hardening of the cerebral arteries causes a psychosis, but the latter is a likely result of the former. This disease differs somewhat from senile dementia discussed above, but also has certain similarities. Psychiatric management of the patient, for instance, is almost the same for both illnesses.

Epilepsy is defined as "a paroxysmal, transitory disturbance of brain function which develops suddenly, ceases spontaneously and exhibits a conspicious tendency to recurrence."[1]/ It is not a disease, but rather a symptom, and includes transient episodes of psychic disturbances. It is divided into two types: One, genuine or idiopathic epilepsy, in which there is no known local, general or psychologic cause; Two, symptomatic epilepsy in which there is an organic basis. Any structural cerebral disorder, no matter how acquired, can cause an epileptic disturbance. Epilepsy is a physico-chemical disturbance in the branch of medicine known as neurology. There are so many possible causes of epilepsy that each case deserves intensive diagnostic study. The epileptic attacks themselves are divided into major or grand mal which is a general convulsion often preceded by symptoms and followed by a state of confusion, and minor or petit mal which gives no warning, is mild in nature and has no sequelae. Great advances in medicine in the past fifty years have greatly changed the therapy of this condition and depending upon the circumstances, the patient can be cured or brought to a point where he can lead a useful life. To sum up, epilepsy is a symptom rather than a disease, and while there is a substantial minority of cases in which structural changes can be traced, called symptomatic, this fraction is constantly increasing as the horizons of neurology and associated specialties widen to increase the general knowledge. But psychiatrists and psychologists are convinced that there is a strong psychic factor in all epilepsy cases, which will remain even after neurological diagnostic tools are improved to near perfection.

There is a large group of chronic neurologic disorders which affect the mind, so large that it can only be glanced at briefly. Dementia is the absence or reduction of intellectual faculties due to known organic brain disease which is irreversible. The individual's reaction to this loss or reduction give rise to symptoms dependent on his previous personality, and often these symptoms are the first outward sign of his illness. Some of these symptoms are loss of recent memory, partial amnesia, difficulty with words or physical movement, etc. Psychic epilepsy is a localized convulsive seizure. Hallucinations are frequent symptoms of convulsive disorders. Brain tumors, usually cause psychiatric symptoms to arise, and can often be diagnosed from these symptoms long before neurologic phenomena have arisen. Vascular diseases (those of blood vessels) exceed in frequency all other brain diseases. These include arteriosclerosis and the so-called "strokes," cerebrovascular accidents as some authors call them[2]/or cerebral hemorrhage, cerebral thrombosis and cerebral embolism.

Encephalitis lethargica is a true neuropsychiatric disease in that it starts with neurological symptoms which are soon interwoven within series of psychiatric manifestations. Encephalitis itself is an inflammation of the brain and is probably of viral origin although there is as yet no certainty.

Its psychiatric symptoms include conduct disorder, depression, hypochondriasis, ophthalmologic complaints, lessened work capacity, Parkinsonism and vegetative disturbances.

The disease is a chronic one and the therapy is on a holistic basis, using psychotherapy, pharmacological therapy, and surgery for advanced cases of Parkinsonism. The general management of the patient is very important.

Psychiatric conditions following head injury is a clinically useful term to describe mental illness caused by a head injury. Due to the importance most people attach to their heads and the sensory organs within, overemphasis is laid upon such an injury and there is a common tendency to ascribe to it any post-traumatic phenomena. Medicine, however, still is ignorant of the physical mechanism of a concussion. The attempt to understand these post traumatic psychiatric conditions is complicated by the fact that many of these injuries occur in industrial, automobile and similar accidents where lawsuits may occur, thus bringing a financial element into the clinical picture, overemphasizing possible malingerings. Here we have strayed into the field of medical jurisprudence, but it is sufficient to point out that a head injury may lead to genuine psychiatric problems, depending on the type of injury and the previous psychiatric state of the injured person.

Acute and chronic alcoholic disorders some times cause abnormal personality patterns. Psychiatrically, any person who drinks sufficiently to impair his efficiency or to interfere with his occupational, social or economic adjustment is an alcoholic.

Alcoholism is both an effect and a cause of personality disorders. Cyclical insane, occasionally schizophrenic, chronic depressive, paranoic, psychoneurotic and sociopathic types frequently become alcoholics as a result of their abnormal personalities. On the other hand, excessive drinking can cause delirium tremens, hallucinosis (usually auditory), diseases of nutritional defects and chronic mental deterioration.

Toxic psychoses, that is, those caused by poison can be grouped by the substances causing the toxicity:

37

1. Drugs, e.g., bromide, barbituates, belladona
2. Hormones used in therapy, e.g., ACTH and cortisone
3. Gases like carbon monoxide
4. Chemicals in industry, such as carbondisulfide
5. Endogenous causes, like fever and uremia
6. Deficiencies such as pellagra and electrolyte imbalance

These psychoses fall into four patterns:

1. Simple intoxication—sluggish but in right mind
2. Delirium of which the hallmark is disorientation
3. Transitory schizophrenia—when appearing acutely in a setting of fever or toxemia, the prognosis is for a quick recovery once the fever or toxemia subside
4. Hallucinosis—good orientation despite the hallucinating

Infective-exhaustive psychoses border on several organic conditions and are grouped together because of similar clinical pictures and for convenience. Under the former are included infections of the central nervous system including meningitis, encephalitis and brain abscess and systemic infections which include most acute infectious febrile diseases. The latter includes postinfections (most chronic infectious diseases), puerperal states, post surgery, miscellaneous and extreme fatigue. The most prominent clinical feature of all these psychoses is delirium. Treatment of these psychoses consists of alleviation of acute symptoms, general supportive measures and specific correction of underlying causes.

Huntington's chorea is classified simply as a chronic brain syndrome of unknown causation and is a clear example of a hereditary mental disorder. It is an irreversible organic psychosis associated with chronic progressive chorea (St. Vitus dance). Personality changes mark the onset of the disease, sometimes with delusional trends developing. Often schizophrenia is the diagnosis based on similarity of symptoms. As the mental symptoms develop, those of chronic progressive chorea begin to appear, although on occasion only the former appear or only the latter. The family history is valuable in making the diagnosis. The prognosis is profound, bedridden dementia, averaging fifteen years to death.

There are certain illnesses and ailments which arise out of metabolic, endocrine and nutritional disorders which lead to psychiatric disorders. They differ from the neuroses and functional psychoses to be considered hereinafter in that there is a definite physical change within the patient prior to the onset of the psychiatric symptoms.

The psychiatric effects of metabolic-endoncrine disease depend on:

1. Specific nature of changes. For example, a disease which produces physical and metabolic retardation like hypothyroidism will probably produce a psychologic reaction of lethargy.

2. The timing of these changes in relation to the stage of growth and level of psychosexual maturity. For example, the problems of puberty in a "normal" person are complicated and fraught with instances of psychiatric disturbance, which are compounded in a person with metabolic-endocrine disorders.

3. Intensity and rate of changes.

4. The stigmatizing nature of the changes, and the reactions of family and peer groups to the stigma. Obviously a metabolic-endocrine disease which produces a deformity, like gigantism or dwarfism will very likely have a psychologic effect.

But most important is the psychologic state of the person prior to the onset of his metabolic-endocrine illness.

Mental deficiency may be defined as a state of arrested or retarded mental development which occurs before adolescence and arises from genetic cause or is induced by disease or injury. Mental defectives are classified as mild or moronic, I.Q. 70-85, some functional impairment; moderate or imbecilic, I.Q. 50-70, functional impairment requiring special training and guidance; severe or idiotic, I.Q. below 50, functional impairment requiring custodial or complete protective care.

Functional Disorders—
The Psychoneuroses

Included herein are conditions allied to the psychoneuroses but which are not themselves psychoneuroses, like some of the neuroses. A pychoneurosis is a psychopathologic syndrome characterized by symptoms such as anxiety, phobias, compulsions and obsessions, but while the psyche is partially disorganized, insight does remain. A psychosis on the other hand usually disrupts all the functions of the psyche.

The so-called war neurosis is one caused by the traumatic incidents of war. The predisposition of the average soldier to acquire this illness depends on his previous psychic state. There are the acute and chronic phases of this neurosis. In the former, where the soldier approaches the breaking point, the symptoms are the outcome of conflict in two areas: 1. The relatedness of the individual to himself and 2. The relatedness to his group. In the latter, the symptoms are less explosive and develop more slowly and usually arise as a result of the individual's altered concept of himself and the outside world. This pathological syndrome then becomes incorporated into the personality in different ways.

Treatment for the acute phase consists of preventing the soldier from admitting that he is defeated. The therapist admits the fear and exhaustion but encourages the soldier that he hasn't reached the breaking point. After a few days of rest and light routine with his unit, the soldier is able to return to full duty.

With chronic cases, those which are permitted to last six months, the prognosis is poor since the soldier has been permitted to develop a pattern of existence in conformity with his reduced resources. This must be broken up and the resistance can be treated by a conscious approach or by barbiturates or hypnosis. Sometimes a combination of all three is used.

Neurasthenia, nervous debility, and hypochrondria, fear of illness, seem to be entirely different functional illnesses, but the similarity of their symptomology makes it logical to group them together. Imaginery somatic aches and pains is the sharpest single symptom which characterizes both functional illnesses. There is also increasing emphasis on the premorbid personality of the subject in diagnosing these illnesses. Some precursors in children are frequent fatigue, aches and pains, gastrointestinal pains, disturbed sleep patterns, etc. However, the distinction between real and imagary illness is unfortunate, since all symptoms are real. A case of this type is very difficult because each must be approached on an individual basis.

Hysteria is marked by a physical manifestation without structural lesion, a calm mental attitude, almost of indifference and episodic mental states where the usual contents of consciousness are partly or completely replaced by a limited but homogeneous group of functions such as fugues, somnambulisms, dream and hypnotic states, etc. To phrase it in another manner, there is a dissociation of mental or bodily functions, and this dissociated function may operate alone or co-existently with normal consciousness. It differs from schizophrenia in that the split-off function is usually a unity and the splitting is seldom in more than two parts.

Motor symptoms include paralysis, tics, tremors, etc. Sensory symptoms include anaesthesia, parasthesia, and hyperesthesia. Visceral symptoms include aneroxia, vomiting, hiccough and various abdominal complaints. Mental symptoms include amnesia, somnambulism, fugues, dream states, hysterical "fits" or attacks, etc. These symptoms correspond strikingly with the usual lay concepts of the disease.

Hysteria can be traced to the climax of infantile sexuality and the oedipus complex with its strivings, counterstrivings and guilt feelings. The prognosis is favorable and usually responds to psychoanalytic psychotherapy.

Fear is a normal emotion and a healthy protective device in helping the individual to avoid a situation fraught with danger. It is grounded in reality. Phobia, on the other hand, is a neurotic fear, of no help to the individual and is infused with fantasy. Freud has been quoted someplace as saying that fear of a lion in the African jungle is normal, whereas fear of the same animal in the streets of London is neurotic. A phobia is a morbid fear associated with morbid anxiety. Here anxiety is not the usual uneasiness that it connotes in the English language, but the translation of the German word **angst** which has a much stronger connotation of fear and would be better translated as terror. Phobias are particularly the mental illness of small children, and so prominent and omnipresent are they that few escape experiencing that degree and kind of fear that is phobic in nature, no matter how short or undestructive the spasm may be.

Anxiety, while a psychoneurosis, can be defined as an affect (the feeling-tone accompaniment of an idea or mental representation) which differs from others in its specific unpleasurable character. Anxiety has bilateral characteristics, somaphysiological, such as disturbed breathing, increased heart activity, vasomotor changes, trembling or paralysis, sweating, etc., and psychological, such as perceptions of specific unpleasurable feelings and sensations, apprehension, etc. Freud believed that anxiety arises automatically whenever the psyche is overwhelmed by an influx of stimuli too great to be mastered or discharged. Such stimuli may be of external or internal origin, but usually from the id or drives. This type of anxiety is called traumatic.

Still another misunderstanding in translation from Freud bedevils the explication of obsessions and compulsions. Freud used the German word **Zwangsneurose** to describe this clinical entity; his London translater used the word obsession whereas his New York translater used the word compulsion. Writers on the subject to the present day still try to differentiate the two[3] while the more historically oriented use the phrase obsession-compulsion. Hereafter, the word obsession will be used and, despite its original designation as a neurosis by Freud, it will be included at this point with the other psychoneuroses.

An obsession is an idea or emotion (an impulse) that persists in the mind of an individual and cannot be ousted by any conscious process. To the conscious, the obsession is uninfluenced by logic or reasoning, and is distinctly unwanted.

It can be experienced by a normal or abnormal person. The former does not interfere substantially with the adequate performance of that person's mental functions. In other words, it is not long lasting, only partly modifies sound thinking and can be minimized or nullified by concentration of interests on other topics. But a morbid obsession essentially controls the conscious realm, is more or less

42

constant in time and compels the individual to act so as to minimize its effects as much as possible.

An obsession usually appears in the form of an idea, strongly charged with emotion. There are intellectual obsessions, such as constant pre-occupation with an intellectual problem, which often leads to incessant activity in an attempt to find the answer. Inhibiting obsessions are made up, for example, of a complex of doubts, fear and scruples which tend to inhibit the individual's activities. Impulsive obsessions are thus designated because they are associated with morbid gratification in action. They are made up of the so-called manias like dipsomania and kleptomania. The usual explanation for obsessions today is concerned with the unconscious. They appear to be the consequences of the release of unrepressed instinctual qualities from their unconscious representation; the released instincts are transformed to the sphere of consciousness usually in conjunction with some idea which has no presumptive relationship (from the patient's standpoint) to the unconscious impulse. The patient cannot understand why he should be obsessed by the thought that does obsess him.

Reactive-depressions occur when a depressive state is directly occasioned by some external situation and is relieved when the external situation is removed. They generate acute feelings of despondency and dysphoria (misery). They can be physiologic (normal) or neurotic. The former is a reaction to life's acute difficulties often caused by the loss of a job or a sex object or the like. The dysphoria is transient and ends with a spontaneous remission without causing a deep rooted change in the patient's life adjustments. The latter in which the dysphoria is very strong may present it as the only symptom, as the first sign of a forthcoming or concurrent somatic or psychic disease or as something hidden behind other psychic or somatic diseases.

Symptoms are diminished activity, lowered self-assurance, apprehension, constricted interests (including sexual) and a general loss of initiative. These symptoms render difficult but not impossible the patient's performance of his everyday tasks.

This ailment, though classed among the psychoneuroses, is not necessarily a serious one, and often clears up in a short period of psychotherapy. This often depends on past events which were traumatic and which supplied the psychologic raw material for subsequent exaggerated reactions. It must also be noted that victims of reactive depression are also victims of an overstrict superego.

There are certain mental illnesses denominated character disorders which will be discussed briefly. They are more or less synonymous with personality disorders and are of the same type as sexual deviations and drug addictions, but not as dramatic or melodramatic. Again, we come to the problem of definition since character has so many meanings and has engaged the attentions of so many disciplines in addition to medicine.

From the non-medical viewpoint, it means a moral and ethical value judgment of behavior. To a specialist in the field of the psyche, it is the structural basis of conduct, largely built up by environmental factors, both accidental and deliberate, which can be relied on as a guide or prophecy of future conduct. However, it seems to be all things to all men in psychiatry, and in defining character types, we must also state whose typology we are using, for example, Freud's, Horney's, etc. It is difficult to define character disorders other than by denominating them. Freud names the genital, anal and oral characters, depending on the patient's fixation on the particular erogenous zone with corresponding traits of hysterical, obsessive and narcissistic. We also find discussions of the impulsive character, the neurotic character and others. Disorders in the character are not usually severe enough to require treatment unless they become morbid, that is, affecting the mind deleteriously or are of the serious type like deviations and addictions mentioned above.

Functional Psychoses

These are the cases of complete disintegration of the personality with no organic cause. Since disease carries the connotation of pathology of the tissues, psychiatrists prefer the

44

term mental disorder where the only pathology is that of the psyche.

Manic depressive psychosis is one of the affective reactions (like involutional psychosis, later described) which does not lead to a true deterioration of the patient as does schizophrenia. It thus includes periodic and circular insanity, simple mania, melancholia, and many types of confusion and delirium. Another distinction between the schizophrenic and manic-depressive psychoses is that while patients suffering from either can entertain diametrically opposite feeling or emotions, the schizophrenic can do so at the same time, whereas the manic depressive has room for only one at a time. The manic-depressive disorder is a psychosis rather than a psychoneurosis, because the patient does not fight it as does the psychoneurotic but adjusts to it and lives in it and is thus completely divorced from it, which is another way of describing a psychosis. The prepossessing symptoms of the disorder are attacks of melancholia and mania, of greater or lesser degree, and usually alternating. Therapy is attuned to the needs of the individual patient, the severity and kind of attack and any predisposing factors. The prognosis is generally favorable, but cannot predict any future attacks of melancholia or mania.

Schizophrenia, formerly called dementia praecox, may be defined as "a specific reaction to an extreme state of anxiety, originated in childhood and reactivated later in life by psychologic factors. The specific reaction consists of the preponderant adoption of mental mechanisms which belong to lower levels of integration. Inasmuch as the result is a regression to, but not an integration at, lower levels, a disequilibrium is engendered which causes further regression."4/ This name of this most important syndrome was changed because profound deterioration (dementia) was not the inevitable end result and because it did not always appear at the time of adolescence. The name schizophrenia was adopted to designate one of the fundamental characteristic of the schizophrenias, the splitting off of portions of the psyche which then dominate the patient's psychic life for a time and lead an independent existence even though these portions may be contrary and contradictory to the personality as a whole.

It is a slowly progressive deterioration of the entire personality which expresses itself in disorders of feelings, thought and conduct and a tendency towards withdrawal from reality. Depending upon the predominant symptoms of any episode, the schizophrenias can be classed as acute or chronic. Symptoms may be divided into fundamental and characteristic, such as disturbances in associations, or affects, of the will and behavior, ambivalence of the affect, intellect or will, autism, attention defects, changes in the person and dementia. Accessory or secondary symptoms, such as hallucinations, delusions, memory disturbances, etc., differ from the primary symptoms in that they appear as well in other classifications of mental disease.

Paranoia is an extremely rare psychosis in which an intricate, complex and logically elaborated delusional system slowly develops, without hallucinations. Superficially, the rest of the personality remains relatively intact, even though the course of the disorder is chronic and protracted. Paranoid states are psychoses characterized by paranoid delusions, neither highly systematized and elaborate, as in paranoia, nor fragmented and bizarre, as in schizophrenia. There is no personality deterioration. This disorder may be of relatively brief duration, although sometimes it becomes chronic. They will be discussed together.

The delusional states which these disorders engender are usually those of persecution and grandiosity, less occasionally of jealousy or erotic thoughts. The delusion of persecution is the classic symptom of paranoia in which the patient builds a whole dream world around this fantasy, believing that every one is an enemy, bent on his destruction, which is at the same time only a part of his personality so that to the outside world, he still presents the facade of his premorbid personality, satisfactory or not as it may be. Since the person likely to develop a form of paranoia is generally a tense, insecure, anxious and fearful person to begin with and has probably met these problems by neurotic adjustments, this personality is probably not a very happy or self-satisfying one. It is therefore difficult to say just when a person passes into the psychotic area of the paranoias. Retrospectively, after a study of a case history, it is simple to pinpoint cause and effect and trace the course of the illness.

Grandiose delusions, neither part of a manic elation nor sufficiently disorganized to be a schizophrenia, are among the psychotic paranoid reactions. They occur infrequently and are among the more serious of the paranoias. The themes of the delusions arise from the patient's surrounding culture including its current folklore and popular literature. The delusions range from a simple conviction of the patient's enormous talent to intricately systematized messianic concepts. They tend to be stable, persistent and well-organized.

The immediate therapeutic goal in paranoid reactions is the reduction of anxiety and the re-establishment of genuine communication. Excessive anxiety lies behind excessive paranoid projection, and both are intimately related to the regression and partial disintegration of personality which have occurred. The delusions, like the tip of an iceberg, are only the visible symptoms of these fundamental processes, the hidden portion of the iceberg.

Involutional psychosis is the term given to any psychiatric disorder arising during the involutional period and presumably associated with it etiologically. The involutional period is the period of menopause in the woman and a psychologic similar, later period in men. Many forms of psychiatric states occur during this period of which two are outstanding. Involutional melancholia is classically an anxious, agitated, delusional depression of the menopause, with a strong tendency toward suicide, quite often with a premorbid personality of insecurity and inhibiting super-ego which is undone by the changes of menopause. Shock treatment and psychotherapy seem to bring the psychosis to a speedy and successful end.

The second state is also a depressive one with elements of the paranoid. This does not include all paranoid reactions during the menopause, but only those representing the true paranoid trend in this period, that is, the physiologic, psychologic, endocrine and other changes are the precipitating causes. There is no drug as yet to counteract all these changes, but purely menopausal symptoms should be treated by endocrine therapy. The prognosis for this psychosis is not as favorable as for the former one.

Personality Disorders

This is a broad group of psychiatric disorders, mostly found in children and adolescents, which are also called psychopathic states and behavior disorders. These disorders are not secondary to somatic diseases or defects nor to convulsive disorders, and are not part of a well-defined psychosis or psychoneurosis. The primary behavior disorders are considered to be reactions to an unfavorable environment; they appear as problems of personality development, as persisting undesirable traits or unfavorable habits, as delinquency or conduct disorders, as certain neurotic traits and as problems of school, general education or vocational difficulties.

Generally speaking, the psychopathic personality has the following characteristics:

1. Superficial charm and good intelligence.
2. Absence of delusions and other signs of irrational thinking.
3. Absence of "nervousness" or other psychoneurotic manifestations.
4. Unreliability.
5. Untruthfulness and insincerity.
6. Lack of remorse or shame.
7. Inadequately motivated anti-social behavior.
8. Poor judgment and failure to learn by experience.
9. Pathologic egocentricity and incapacity for love.
10. General poverty in major affective reactions.
11. Specific loss of insight.
12. Unresponsiveness in general interpersonal relations.
13. Fantastic and uninviting behavior with drink and sometimes without.
14. Suicide rarely carried out.

15. Sex life impersonal, trivial and poorly integrated.

16. Failure to follow any life plan.

The etiology of this disorder is unknown; some writers claim it to be organic, others purely psychogenic. As is obvious in this discussion, it is a subject that falls within the provinces of social psychiatry and criminology as well as psychiatry. Technically, the psychopath is sane, absent other psychiatric symptoms.

Psychosomatic Medicine

This term is used to describe a number of illnesses where emotional and personality disorders result in physiologic dysfunction and structural change. It is generally considered an unfortunate word because it emphasizes a non-existent dichotomy, as if illnesses were either of psychologic or physiologic origin. No somatic disease is entirely free of psychic influence; in even the purest psychic disturbance, there are organic-constitutional factors, somatic compliance, etc. But this approach to a patient, combining physiology and psychology in a holistic method, under whatever terminology is used, is one of medicine's newest weapons against disease, and is teaching doctors many new things about specialties of medicine that were previously unknown.

This term is also broad enough to include an initial organic illness which laters develops psychiatric elements. Cardiovascular disturbances are a prime example, since anyone with a heart condition will undoubtedly develop emotions, mostly morbid, about his health. Thus the cardiologist, originally consulted for an organic disturbance, must call upon psychiatric knowledge, his own or a psychiatrist's, to cure his patient or restore him to a viable equilibrium.

Many physical illnesses have long been recognized to be psychogenic in origin, such as ulcers, essential hypertension, rheumatoid arthritis, ulcerative colitis, bronchial asthma, hyperthyroidism and spastic colon. Some respiratory disorders are now being found to have a psychiatric as well as physiologic basis. These include breath-holding attacks, the hyperventilation syndrome, respiratory allergy, vasomotor rhinitis, the common cold, chronic smoker's syndrome, bronchitis, pneumonia and finally and unexpectedly pulmonary tuberculosis itself.

Sexual functions, are a combination of a set of psychic and physiological stimuli which are links in a chain of interrelated conditioned reflexes. Thus any disturbance of this chain, somatic or psychic, will lead to a disturbance or dysfunction of the sexual function. However, structural damage to the sex organs occurs infrequently and is easily diagnosed, so that most so-called sex problems, impotence in men and frigidity in women are the chief ones, come in the field of the psyche rather than the soma.

Finally in the field of psychosomatic medicine, there is the disturbance of the body image. As we grow and develop, each person acquires an innate conception of his physical body in space, usually as a social creation as he meets and mingles with others. When this concept is suddenly and rudely disturbed by physical changes due to neurologic diseases, with the sensory or motor system connected with movement or posture, toxic or metabolic disorders, progressive deformities caused by other somatic illnesses, acute dismemberment of a part of the body or personality disorders like psychoses, there is usually a severe psychiatric disorder. The "phantom limb" where pain is felt in an absent limb is one dramatic manifestation. Here the patient is taught to accept his new state and become adjusted to it.

Conclusion

The present and preceding chapters have convered the subject of psychiatry exhaustively, although condensed, from almost every possible angle. The reader who has completely absorbed this material is a knowledgeable, albeit non-professional, student of the field, and the importance of this is self-evident. But the greater importance and the greater utilization of this knowledge lies in its application to, and fusion with, the law, especially the substantive law of insanity. How is this knowledge of psychiatry to be used in the field of law? As explained in the following chapters, the question at issue is not whether a person is sane or insane, but what privileges, liabilities and immunities are granted him, and here the tail tends to wag the dog.

In describing mental disorders and different therapies, it was necessary to categorize them and after proper labeling, to put them in boxes. But life is not that simple. We cannot pin a mental disorder on a person, decide that this one does not affect the ability to think and therefore this man's will is valid. Instead we must use a holistic approach, study all angles of the case and then come to a conclusion. Let us examine the last thing we studied, the disturbance of body image. Superficially a man who has just lost a leg through surgical amputation has the capacity to make a will. But if this set off psychiatric disturbances causing him to hate his children for a fancied neglect of his diabetic condition and he then makes a new will disinheriting them, quaere? Let it again be emphasized as it is continuously throughout this book, each case or situation involving insanity is sui generis and must be examined carefully, completely and with no preconceived notions.

Footnotes

1/ In Hinsie & Campbell, "Psychiatric Dictionary."
2/ *Ibid.*
3/ See, for example, the definition of compulsion in "Psychiatric Dictionary" at page 144 where it is defined among other things as the result of an obsession and "they (the compulsions) are obsessions in action."
4/ Sylvano Arieti at page 501 of "American Handbook of Psychiatry."

Part II—INSANITY, PROCEDURAL LAW

Chapter 4

SCOPE OF PART II—INTRODUCTION

We have covered the psychiatric portion of this book and now approach the law portions. The subject of law is divided, as is the usual bar examination, into two parts, substantive law and procedural law, sometimes called adjective law.

Substantive law is the rule of law applicable to a particular situation, in litigation, or in non-litigious situations such as drafting a contract or will where reference must be made to the law applicable to a given situation. While all legal situations are subject to judicial decisions or case law, as the law student learns it, these in turn are divided into case law based on a statute or constitution, federal or state, and interpretation thereof as in Constitutional law and case law based on previously decided cases which have gradually been built up into a body of law called precedents as in contract law. The latter is called common law to distinguish from the former or statutory law. Often criminal law is an example of both. Originally it was built up as a body of precedents based on moral judgments of the times. Later it was codified and the code of criminal law specifically stated that it was exclusive and not based upon the previous common law or precedents. Yet in interpreting the newly enacted statutory law, the courts were often forced to go back to common law to fill in interstices left by the statutory law or to better explicate its provisions, while at the same time trying to hew to the statutes and give them lip service.

Procedural law is strictly forensic in that it applies only in cases arising out of litigation, and consists of the ways and means by which, in an orderly fashion, the substantive law governing the situation is properly applied thereto.

Of course, procedural law governs only that part of substantive law which is applied to a forensic or litigated situation.

While these two parts of the law, substantive and procedural, are usually defined in that order, this book will study procedural law first, since this gets right to the point of how the general public or society treats the psychotic or quasi-psychotic persons in the courts and institutions. This leads to a discussion of forensic psychiatry, or psychiatry in the courts, which is the core of this book, appearing in Chapter 6, below. To properly place it in context many other subjects have been and will be discussed both before and after Chapter 6 in order to exhaustively elucidate it.

In the law of insanity, which is not one of the classical divisions of the body of law such as contracts or torts but which cuts across such classical divisions, there is a meeting of law and sociology. Just as a marriage contract involves three persons, the bridal pair and the state or organized community, the law of insanity involves the state as well because in a modern civilization, the community takes a quasi-paternalistic interest in various handicaps of its citizens and resident aliens. In order to define what we mean by society, we must refer back to the first chapter and our definition of law. There we posited a tripartite community or entity consisting of a polity whose function is maintaining peace and order internally, and an economy and a society which were not defined at that point. We now remedy this deliberate oversight.

The economy is defined for the purposes of this book as that part of the entity which provides the needs of the community, the necessities in a simple, rudimentary one, necessities and desired luxuries in a complex world such as America today. In a capitalistic society such as ours, these necessities and luxuries are largely supplied by private enterprise but several are supplied by the entity such as mail service and many are regulated or subsidized by it like public utilities and airlines respectively. While the economy is not the subject of this book, the astute reader will have noticed that Harry Stock Sullivan's interpersonal approach discussed

53

above in Chapter II names these basic necessities as man's basic drives or "satisfactions" and that Erich Fromm's cultural approach discussed in the same chapter, severely criticizes America's cultural attitudes which he blames for a large part of America's neuroses. Parenthetically the interrelation of a success-oriented economy which also coincides with many of man's basic needs with psychiatry which considers these aims and needs as affecting a man's personality would make the subject of a book in itself, "Psychiatry and the Economy."

The society is the remaining portion of the entity after the polity and economy are taken out. Briefly it is that part of the community which seeks the higher things in life for the betterment of its members beyond what they are getting in the way of protection and peacekeeping and the furnishings of necessities. It is the difference between savagery and civilization and the size of an entity's society is the measure of its civilization. Society is a very ambiguous word, and since it often is used in the sense defined above and sometimes in the sense that an entity or community has been defined out of which the polity and economy arise, it has been necessary to specifically define it as above. And just as political science is the study of the polity and economics the study of the economy, so sociology is the study of the society.

Thus when it was said above in effect that the law of insanity is a fusion of law and society, it is meant that the strict definition of law in Chapter 1 above is ameliorated somewhat by the higher aims of the society. While part of the entity, it is a sort of two-headed creature combining elements from the polity (law) and society. It is also very close to the classical legal branch of Constitutional Law and rights and privileges thereunder, since in order to physically protect the vast majority of the members of the community it is forced to limit the freedom of a small number of members, and freedom is the be-all and end-all of most polities, especially one such as America's. The law of domestic relations, that which covers the relations between married couples, their children and the community, the substantive and procedural law of which have been codified recently in

New York's Family Court Act and in similar statutes in other states, has similar situations where legal and social factors are fused together. It must be emphasized that judicial decisions in insanity and family cases are usually quasi-judicial in nature, since they are sui generis, that is, independent of other decisions, thus standing on their own feet and based more on medical, psychiatric and social considerations rather than legal ones.

Definitions

This is a tremendous part of law, even though quantitively it is smaller than substantive law. The distinction is somewhat equivalent to that between the end of a journey and the route by which it is reached, with this difference, that the route taken may determine the destination. Thus, the care of a possible incompetent and whether or not he is hospitalized or requires it may well have a powerful evidentiary effect on the substantive legal questions of his responsibility in a criminal or civil case.

The potential incompetent's interlocutary rights, that is, rights before final adjudication, can be affected by the care and disposition of him. Obviously, when he is hospitalized, his position and opportunity to protect himself are less than if he is under the care of a relative or friend in the outside world, and the stigma of hospitalization may have a serious and lasting effect upon a borderline case.

In any commitment proceeding involving a potential incompetent, there is a very grave danger that his constitutional rights and privileges may be abused and as will be seen later both the substantive and procedural statutes governing the handling of potential incompetents are filled with safeguards for his protection.

In conclusion, it must be emphasized that time and certainty are essential for the well-being of a potential incompetent. Unnecessary delays and the creation of uncertainties, especially in a borderline case, are bound to have a deleterious effect on any potential incompetent. Relatives, friends and attorneys of any such person must be vigilant to see that a "clean" procedural record is maintained, that is, that the proceedings are kept as simple and uncomplicated as possible, that no legal cross-currents or competing jurisdictions be permitted to crop up and that the health and well being of the potential incompetent be kept uppermost in mind.

Chapter 5

CARE OF INCOMPETENTS

Under this chapter heading is included the incompetent's relations with others and with the community's machinery set up to provide for his safety and well being. Obviously, this is the social portion of the entity despite the fact that it is set up in forensic form and thus appears to be part of the polity or legal portion of the entity. Incompetent will be used to refer to a person already committed to a mental institution or judicially declared to be one; otherwise as a potential incompetent, he will be denominated a patient. Since New York State has one of the most modern statutory systems of handling incompetents, which became effective in September 1965, which is a model-statute being used by many other states the following discussion is based on these statutes, but where other states differ substantially, this will be indicated.

Home Care

Obviously the best place for the care of a patient, whether at the onset of mental illness or after discharge from a mental hospital as cured, is his normal environment, his home with parents or friends if single, with his wife and children if married. This decision cannot be made by lay-men no matter how close they are to the patient or how well they think they know him. A general practitioner of medicine must be consulted and he should further call in a psychiatrist to be consulted. Then if these medical specialists decide that the patient is not potentially dangerous to him-self or others, he can continue in his present environment under the joint stewardship of his closest relative or friend with whom he has been living and these two doctors, with outside psychiatric treatment at a clinic or with a private doctor to reverse the course of his illness. Note that in this stage of the patient's care, everything is private, the community not entering the picture with its courts or formal social services, but only informally in the setting up of mental health clinics and other services for mentally ill people. However, as will be discovered in Chapter 8 in the Substantive Law portion of this book on the torts of an incompetent, if the patient remains in his original environment under the presumed care of a friend or relative whom the law denominates a custodian, the latter is liable for negligence in controlling the patient. This is discussed below, in the above cited chapter. Paradoxically, an institution guilty of negligence in discharging an incompetent is not legally responsible for any tort committed by him after his discharge.

Non-Judicial Commitments 1/

These are divided into voluntary and involuntary types. Even a casual reader of the daily newspapers of any large city is aware of this subject of non-judicial commitments since there are many stories of people undergoing sudden and acute mental disturbances who wind up in mental institutions either on their own initiative or aided by policemen who by the nature of their duties have been forced to become curbstone psychiatrists. And periodically there are news articles relating the mental health facilities of the city and advice as to what to do and where to go when a person undergoes a sudden and violent mental disturbance.

Voluntary Commitment

In a voluntary commitment, informality is the password. Any person (the parent, legal guardian or next of kin of a minor) may voluntarily apply to any hospital for admission as a mental patient and the hospital must receive him if he is suitable for care and treatment. Such voluntary patient may leave at any time but in the discretion of the hospital director, he may be kept for a period of fifteen days for such care and treatment and thereafter until ten days after receipt of notice by him from the patient of his desire to leave. Within this period or a reasonable one, the hospital must arrive at one of three decisions: one, the patient is a proper member of the voluntary or informal class and this care and treatment continues; two, he is not sufficiently ill to belong to this class and is therefore discharged; three, he is too ill for this type of informal therapy and requires hospitalization under another section of Article V (to be covered hereafter). If a person other than the patient (or the parent, legal guardian or next of kin of a minor) makes an application to discharge the patient, the hospital can refuse this request, subject to judicial review if requested by the applicant. Any patient admitted by a hospital under these circumstances must be informed of these rights of his upon his admission.

Generally speaking, this section of Article V is a simple one designed to cover the situation where a patient, whether in some form of psychotherapy or not, suddenly believes he cannot handle the problems of his life and needs help urgently. This usually occurs in those dark hours of night when pessimism and despair are most rife and the usual medical, religious, social or psychiatric aids cannot be reached. It is a sensible and intelligent means to give aid and comfort to these suddenly troubled persons.

Involuntary Commitments—Non-Judicial

Heretofore, we divided the subject into non-judicial and judicial commitments, the former voluntary and involuntary. But since all judicial commitments are per se involuntary, we are now considering them together without changing the previous classifications, non-judicial and judical commitments, under the subject of involuntary commitments.

Non-judicial are to a certain extent quasi-judicial since they are subject to judicial review, as was the subject of voluntary commitments as to one point (see supra same page, line 11), but since they are initiated outside the court or extraforensically, non-judicial can still be used without confusion. There are four types:

1. Admission on the certificate of two physicians,
2. Admission on the certificate of one physician,

3. Admission on the certificate of a health officer,
4. In case of an emergency.

In the case of admission on the certificate of two physicians, an application must be made to a hospital by a close relative, person with whom he resides, the committee of his person, etc., stating the facts on which the need for commitment is based. Upon receipt of the application and the two physicians' certificate, the hospital must admit the patient and examine him to determine if he needs psychiatric care and treatment. If it is determined that he be admitted and the patient or a relative or friend requests his release, there is a hearing before a court to determine if he should be released or retained further. At the end of sixty days, the hospital, if no previous hearing on a request for release has been made, must determine the future hospitalization of the patient. If he is agreeable, the patient may stay on as voluntary patient, except that unlike a voluntarily committed patient, he cannot leave of his own volition but must apply to a court himself or through a relative or friend. If the patient disagrees, the hospital must apply to a court for an order authorizing the retention of the patient, and this court order can be appealed within thirty days by the patient, relative or friend to a different judge in the same court who causes the issue of competence to be tried before a jury.

The situation in the case of an admission on the certificate of one physician is very similar to the above except that in this case, the patient consents to the admission. The application for admission is almost identical. If later on, the patient changes his mind, another doctor's certificate to the effect that he is in need of psychiatric care and treatment must be obtained. Thereafter his case proceeds in the same fashion as if he had not previously consented and a certificate from two physicians had been filed, and with the same rights to judicial review that are present in the two physician situation. However, if he does consent, his situation is still different than if he had been originally a voluntarily admitted patient and he cannot be discharged solely on his own volition. It is obvious that in the beginning at least, the type of patient in the one physician situation is sicker than the voluntary patient, since he requires the help of one physician and a relative or friend to be admitted to a hospital; even though later on, he may be retained by a hospital on a voluntary basis and is thus in a situation similar to the original volunteer, he never achieves the latter's rights to leave on his own volition (which of course is subject to procedural safeguards).

In the case of admission on the certificate of a health officer, there is an element of emergency involved. The application must show that the patient is dangerous to himself or others and needs immediate care and treatment due to mental illness. The admitting hospital must confirm the element of immediacy. Within fifteen days if it is decided to continue retention of the patient and he disagrees, a certificate of another physician in support of the application must be filed. Thereafter, the case continues on the same basis as if the patient had been originally admitted on the certificate of two physicians with the same judicial safeguards as in the latter's case.

Emergency admissions come under two headings:

1. Actions of the director of a psychiatric hospital
2. Actions of a police officer

The director of a psychiatric hospital may receive and retain therein any person alleged to need immediate observation, care or treatment for mental illness for a period of thirty days. If at any time after admission, the patient or anyone on his behalf gives notice of his desire to be released or before the expiration of the thirty day period the hospital director determines to keep the patient for treatment beyond the thirty day period and the patient disagrees, an application for hospitalization on a two physician certificate must be made and thereupon the two physician certificate procedure including court authorization and judicial review is followed. Despite this safeguard of court authorization and judicial review, this is a poorly worded and vague section of the law (MHL Sec. 78 subd. 1) since it doesn't specify who the person is who may allege that a person requires "immediate observation, care or treatment for mental illness." Is he a qualified psychiatrist or a layman relative or friend whose interest may be different or even diametrically opposed to that of the patient. And how is the director of a psychiatric hospital "to receive and retain patients"?

The chances are that the passive sounding verb "receive" will actually require a very active form of conduct on the part of the director and his associates and assistants. This can be enough to throw a borderline, only slightly bewildered patient into a very severe traumatic psychosis. This subdivision is so vague and uncertain as to be almost unconstitutional and it is hoped that the legislature will amend this part of the law so as to make it more definite and certain.

Any peace officer can take into custody, that is, arrest, any person appearing to be mentally ill and conducting himself in a manner which would be disorderly if he were sane and see that he is placed in a psychiatric hospital. This subdivision (3) of Section 78 is a very simple and precise one and we know exactly the two ways in which it will operate. If the patient is obviously mentally ill, as a would-be suicide for example, the peace officer rescues him and sees that he is taken to a psychiatric hospital. On the other hand, if the emphasis is first on the disorderly conduct, as in the case of indecent exposure, and the patient is first arrested on this charge, and then it becomes apparent to the arresting officer or one of his superiors or to a court attendant or a committing magistrate that the putative criminal is suffering from mental illness, at that point he will be sent to a psychiatric institution. Thus this portion is very clear and very simple.

Judicial Commitments

These are of course also involuntary. They are of two kinds, immediate, issuing out of the magistrates' courts and formal, arising in the State Supreme Court, the general court of original jurisdiction.

The magistrate comes into the picture in the following ways. Whenever he is informed that a person is apparently mentally ill, he may issue a bench warrant directing that such person be brought before him. If at that time, such person appears to be mentally ill, the magistrate issues a civil order directing such patient's removal to a psychiatric hospital pursuant to Section 78. Such case would come under subdivision 1 thereof discussed above at page 61 and would obviate the vagueness and uncertainty complained of at that point.

In a criminal action before a magistrate, if the defendant appears to be mentally ill and the court decides either that there is no crime or no sufficient cause to hold this defendant guilty, the magistrate may issue a civil order as above directing his committal to a psychiatric hospital with similar safeguards, in which case the criminal action terminates. In other criminal actions before a magistrate where the defendant appears to be mentally ill, the court may issue an order in the criminal action directing the patient's commitment to a psychiatric hospital to determine whether he is mentally ill and report back to the court within thirty days, and in this instance, the patient is also a prisoner. The magistrate's intercessions, like all matters before him, are of an urgent nature and are also controlled by the rules of the magistrates' courts.

We now have reached the subject of formal judicial commitments of incompetents and in New York, these are covered by Article 5A, Mental Hygiene Law, formerly Sections 1356-1358 and 1384 of the Civil Practice Act and vest jurisdiction in its courts of general original jurisdiction, the Supreme Court and the County Courts outside New York City as pointed out above. If a person is incompetent to manage himself and his affairs by reason of age, drunkenness, mental illness or other cause, the courts are granted jurisdiction over the custody and property of that person. "The court shall preserve the property of a person it declares incompetent" and in effect, such person becomes a ward of the court, as in the case of an infant, and the court may appoint a committee of the person or of the property, who may be the same individual. 2/

Any person may commence a special proceeding to declare a person incompetent and to appoint a committee for him by filing a petition which alleges facts showing incompetence, the name and address of his spouse, his known distributees, the nature and value of his property and what property has been conveyed during the period of incompetency and for what value. When the case comes before the court, the judge, in his discretion, may dismiss the petition. Otherwise, there is a trial by jury either before the court or before commissioners. If it appears that any person has acquired property from an incompetent during the period of his incompetency for an inadequate consideration, he may be enjoined from disposing of it and a temporary receiver of the property appointed pending the trial of the issue of incompetency. If a person is a lawfully admitted or committed resident of a state mental hospital under any procedure outlined above, a petition to have appointed a committee of his person or property may be filed by a state officer, on behalf of the state, having jurisdiction over the hospital where the incompetent resides, or an officer of that hospital. If the incompetent is a resident of a mental hospital on a voluntary basis, he must consent to this petition.

A committee of an incompetent is a fiduciary like a testamentary trustee and there are provisions as to bonding. filing accountings, inventories, discovery proceedings, compensation, etc. similar to those governing other fiduciaries. The committee is discharged under the following circumstances:

1. Death of incompetent, in which instance the committee must provide for his burial out of available assets.

2. Incompetent has been declared competent or where he has been discharged from the hospital and is able adequately to conduct his business and personal affairs, in either of which case, the committee must restore to him the property remaining in his hands after a final accounting.

3. The assets of the incompetent have become depleted and a committee is no longer needed.

Release

The director of a mental hospital can discharge any incompetent patient except one held on a criminal charge, as follows:

1. A patient who, in his judgment, is recovered

2. A patient who in his judgment, is not mentally ill

3. An unrecovered patient whose discharge, in the judgment of the director, will not be detrimental to the public welfare or injurious to the patient.3/ Where the director is unwilling to release a patient upon his or another's request and the usual means of judicial review provided the former are presently unavailable and will be so for thirty days, any judge of a court of record, after a hearing in which the facts are ascertained and the hospital director heard, may direct the release of that patient. Where a patient is released, as above described, the release can be permanent, or on a temporary basis for a certain period, subject to home custody and regular check-ups at the hospital.

A criminal psychotic who has been confined to a state mental hospital for the criminally insane such as Mattawan or Dannemora will be returned to a state prison if he recovers before the term of his sentence. If at the termination of his sentence, he is still psychotic, he may be retained in that hospital if the superintendant thinks it is necessary, in which case, he obtains a certificate from two psychiatrists not connected with his hospital and applies to a judge of a court of record for permission. If at the termination of his sentence or later on, the superintendant is of the opinion that the patient can be discharged into the custody of relations or friends with reasonable safety, he can discharge him permanently or temporarily.

Where a defendant is on trial for a criminal act and he pleads insanity as a defense, the jury must be instructed that if it acquits on that ground, it must so state in its verdict. If it does so, and it deems his discharge dangerous to the public peace and safety, the court must commit him to a state lunatic asylum until he becomes sane.4/ This question of later sanity or insanity can be reviewed by a court under the writ of habeas corpus.

After the arrest of any person for a crime, irrespective of whether or not he was insane at the time of the commission of the alleged crime, if at any time prior to or during the trial, it shall appear to the committing magistrate or presiding judge that there is a reasonable ground to believe that the defendant is in such a state of insanity as to preclude him from understanding the charge or making his defense, he may order a psychiatric examination of the defendant. If found to be insane, he is committed to a state mental institution until he recovers in which case, he is returned to his original custody to stand trial on the original charge. If found to be sane by such examination, the criminal proceedings continue as if such psychiatric examination had not occurred.

Writ of Habeas Corpus

This is a legal procedure often used in insanity situations to review the detention of a person. It is an extraordinary, high perogative, common law writ of ancient origin. It is the precious safeguard of personal liberty, jealously guarded by the courts against weakening or dilution. It is a summary remedy, not an action or suit, though sometimes called one of the latter for special purposes. It is a collateral remedy, arising independently and not as part of another action or proceeding.

It is neither a writ of error nor appeal and thus not available for the reversal of mistakes of law or fact in lower courts, but reviews rather jurisdictional matters. It is a civil remedy, no matter whether the prisoner be detained under civil or criminal process. It is a legal remedy, antedating Magna Carta and thus the split between law and equity which arose in England in the Sixteenth Century. It is preserved by the Constitution of the United States in Article I Section 9 thereof, thus attesting to its importance and safeguard of liberty.

It is designed to give an incarcerated person immediate review of the legality of his detention and issues only where all other methods of review have been exhausted. It is the one writ, after other remedies have been exhausted, to review the detention of a person as insane. If a procedure to commit a person as insane is void or jurisdictionally defective, habeas corpus will lie, and the question of insanity is immaterial. On the other hand, if all the requirements of due process are met, it will not lie and it cannot be used as a substitute for a lunacy proceeding. Where an appellate court is granted supervisory jurisdiction over lower courts' guardianship matters, this jurisdiction can be invoked by habeas corpus. And where a person is confined as legally insane and now claims a return to sanity, habeas corpus is the usual method of reviewing his contention.

Constitutional Law [5]/

Here we are concerned not with the classical constitutional law of interpretations of constitutional limitations, police power, states' rights, etc. argued by frock coated lawyers before black robed justices in high ceilinged courtrooms, but with the guts of liberty and due process on the lowest level of the individual's immediate deprivation of his own freedom. Any one, in our type of democracy, who is about to be deprived of his liberty, has in a broad sense a constitutional problem. In ordinary criminal law whose outlines as to personal arrest are fairly clear, the constitutional problems are relatively minor.

But in the case of a potential incompetent, especially a borderline case, who is about to be subjected to personal restraint, a very delicate legal, social and medical problem is presented, which very often must be solved immediately. It is generally not thought of as a constitutional problem, yet any legal process that can cause a person to be deprived of his liberty does raise questions of constitutional law, especially in cases of insanity which do not involve criminal law. Unfortunately, the law has historically dealt with the insane as a species of quasi-criminal, often incarcerating them in so-called hospitals where conditions were far worse than those in prisons for criminals. And always, the law has emphasized a legalistic approach, giving only limited lip service to the social and medical problems involved.

But the advances made by the science of psychiatry and other disciplines connected with the treatment of the insane, plus the interest of a growingly enlightened general public has slowly influenced judges and legislatures to take a more modern approach. The problem is basically threefold: 1. A sound statutory basis for the treatment of incompetents at all stages of their illness, grounded upon the most modern psychiatric and sociological studies; 2. A sound and learned judiciary, trained in basic psychiatric and sociological principles who will administer the laws fairly and justly so as to protect both the general public and the incompetents and their families; 3. An emergency system of public officials which will immediately go to the aid of an incompetent to protect his legal rights.

The statutory problem is slowly and surely being solved and more and more legislatures, judging by statutes enacted by them, are swinging from a penology oriented law of insanity to a sociologic oriented one. Education, publicity and the general feeling of the enlightened public are bringing new concepts into the halls of legislatures and the minds of people.

The judicial problem, while improving as the calibre of the judiciary is improved, is still not being treated in the modern manner that it should be. Problems of incompetents come up at all phases of a case before different judges and magistrates none of whom has had any special training in psychiatry and sociology. The solution is a simple one, to set up special courts like New York's Family Court, to handle only cases of incompetents, to be staffed as in that court by specially trained judges, psychologists, clerks and aides. Only then will the legal problems of incompetents be supervised in an enlightened, intelligent and reasonably consistent manner.

The last problem, emergency legal help, is one on which very little has been done. But again, an innovation can solve the problem quickly and simply. There is a growing publicizing of, and demand for, the establishment of the ombudsman system, a public office of public defenders to right wrongs of all types which has been set up in several

Scandinavian countries. There has long been an outcry of the liberal, progressive forces in this country for the establishment of some system of public defenders to protect the individual's rights and prerogatives granted him by our federal and state constitutions. Nowhere is there a greater need for such an institution than in the case of an incompetent. Whether it is done for him by a separate defender organization or as part of a general public defender system, whether it is done in a form similar to the ombudsman system or some other, the incompetent must be given emergency legal protection as he is already being given emergency medical assistance, and as promptly as possible.

Incompetent Veterans

The legislatures of the federal government and the states, the courts, administrative bodies, similar governmental agencies and the general public have always been careful and considerate of the rights and prerogatives of the men and women who have served in our armed forces during time of war, and rightly so, and this has been especially true of those unfortunate veterans who are today suffering from mental illness, whether as a result of their wartime service or not.

These incompetent veterans are eligible of course for all the benefits and services available to any incompetent as outlined previously in this chapter. In addition under the United States Code, Title 38, Veterans' Benefits, there are special sections 3201-3204 which cover the cases of incompetent veterans. In New York, special benefits for an incompetent veteran appear in Article 5B of the Mental Hygiene Law. They give him special but similar consideration to that given a non-veteran incompetent, but 5B governs where there is a conflict between different articles and sections of the law. The principal problem here is the appointment of a special guardian for the incompetent to receive moneys as a fiduciary for the incompetent veteran where the federal law requires that money be paid to him and that as an incompetent, a special guardian be appointed to receive the money as a condition precedent to its being paid out.

The application and the judicial decision must allege and adjudge two things:

1. The incompetent's right to receive money from the Veterans Administration

2. The incompetent must have been adjudged to be incompetent.

The judgment of incompetence is made by the Veterans Administration under laws regulating it. However, the guardian is appointed by a state court, usually the domicile of the incompetent, that is his legal place of residence.

Perils of Incompetents

There is no better place to discuss some of the dangers lurking for an incompetent than the close of a chapter on the care of incompetents, and while the subtitle is somewhat melodramatic, it is nevertheless an appropriate one.

Up to this point of this chapter, and in fact in the entire book, there has been the assumption, which appears even in statutes, that an incompetent's family and psychiatrist are on his side and are doing their utmost to help him. But in the annals of fiction—novels, plays, stories, motion pictures and television—and in real life which tries so desperately to emulate fiction, the reverse is often true. A fairly common type of incompetent is an elderly, well-to-do, collateral relative with no direct heirs and with substantial wealth which in the normal course of events would descend to his collateral relatives. While a normal, fairly warm relationship usually exists between the older relative and his collateral relatives while the former is of sound mind, the picture often tends to change when increasing age and mental illness take hold. Whatever warm and cordial relationship existed previously is warped and then destroyed by the illness. Increasingly difficult and often mandatory duties on the part of the younger relatives replace their previously simple, voluntary and family activities on behalf of the older person. The assets of the older person, which rightly or wrongly the younger think of as becoming theirs eventually, begin to be dissipated in seemingly unwarranted investments, medical and legal fees and poor pecuniary housekeeping. And finally, the prospect of the older person's imminent death grows increasingly remote, as, with the stresses and strains of ordinary life removed as he moves farther into a world of complete irresponsibility and fantasy, his physical health seems to improve out of all reason and expectation.

It is at this point that the younger relatives, not necessarily with malice, often step in and try to hospitalize the older one and take over his assets as fiduciary to conserve them. Often, there is much to be said on their side, especially where the older persons's sickness is quite advanced, his obligations to his collateral relatives are morally, albeit not legally, strong and there is a grave and present danger that his assets may be dissipated by improper investments or personal liaisons, friendship or even marriage. While the statutes, as pointed out above in this chapter, make careful provision for the protection of incompetents, this is not sufficient because the legislature and courts cannot always foresee every possible situation in which the incompetent may be endangered by those around him and incapable of invoking the judicial protection afforded him.

The danger is greatly enhanced where the incompetent's own psychiatrist or the superintendant of the mental hospital where he is resident or both are of a venal character, easily suborned to crime by collateral relatives intent on obtaining complete mastery of their relative and his assets. There are so many sections of the statutes in question that rely on the opinions and judgments of a hospital superintendant that he must be carefully supervised by both the department in charge of mental hospitals and the legislature, despite the safeguards of his professional training and standing. As for psychiatrists, unfortunately, by its nature, the profession is somewhat infested with "quacks" who, because of its subjective nature, make a very substantial living and even acquire formidable reputations by catering to the gullibility of wealthy, spoiled and self-obsessed patients. Of course, there is quite a gap between a "quack" preying on gullible patients and a psychiatrist who is willing to cross the line into criminal activities to aid unscrupulous relatives in

71

illegally and unjustly hospitalizing a wealthy older relative for the purpose of gaining control of his assets, the fact that there are such weak characters in the profession heightens the danger.

One answer to these problems is the establishment of the public defender system advocated above. By keeping a constant record and surveillance of the whereabouts, mental health and general situation of every incompetent, whether cured or not, probably all problems involving the exploiting and tyrannizing of mentally ill people would be solved.

But the eternal vigilance of legislatures, government departments, courts, administrative bodies, distant relatives and friends can never be relaxed in the unfortunate problems of caring for the mentally ill.

Footnotes

1/This subject of the hospitalization of the mentally ill is covered by New York's Mental Hygiene Law, Article 5.
2/New York Mental Hygiene Law, Section 100.
3/New York Mental Hygiene Law, Section 87.
4/Some states make this permissive instead of mandatory.
5/Cf. Hearings on Constitutional Rights of the Mentally Ill before the Subcommittee on Constitutional Rights of the Senate Committee of the Judiciary 87th Congress 1st Session Pt. 1 (1961).

Chapter 6

FORENSIC PSYCHIATRY

Since the subject of this monograph is basically forensic psychiatry, this is the core of the book, yet is meaningless to the general reader without the chapters that have preceded it and those which will follow. Yet despite its obvious importance, it is a comparatively simple chapter after the complicated and necessarily abridged chapters on psychiatric theory and disorders and preceding the chapters on the substantive law of insanity.

Basically, forensic psychiatry is the science of psychiatry as it appears in court, the impinging or fusing of it on the discipline of law. This is done by psychiatry being applied to the substantive law of the facts before the court, and it is made available to the court by psychiatry through the means of one or more psychiatrists' testifying as to the psychiatric theory, practice and lore applying to the facts before the court. Essentially the testimony of a psychiatrist is based on his opinion of how psychiatry views the facts before the court.

However, opinion evidence is generally inadmissible in court since it is desired that admissable evidence be limited to material, relevant and competent statements of fact from which factual conclusions may be drawn. But there are several exceptions to this rule and one of them permits testifying in the form of an opinion by an expert on the subject in question.

Therefore, a psychiatrist who is desired as a witness concerning his specialty must first be qualified as an expert witness. This is simple since the psychiatrist recites from the witness stand his education, training and background, similar to the resume he inserts in medical reference books. In addition, it is well to have the psychiatrist testify as to his experience as a forensic psychiatrist, that is, the number of times he has appeared as such expert witness and a brief description of the subjects involved. Needless to say, all this precedes his actual testimony or opinion offered by him. Occasionally his qualifications are stipulated by both attorneys.

When his actual testimony on the question in issue is reached, namely, the mental capacity of the party needed to fix his responsibility, we come upon a strange animal in the law of evidence, namely, the hypothetical question. The expert witness must base his opinion on factual data supplied by other evidence, real, testimonial or circumstantial. Since the worth and validity of this other evidence is ultimately to be judged by the jury, on direct examination, the attorney presenting the expert witness to the court must indicate the conditional or hypothetical nature of the expert's opinion by presenting it in the form of a hypothetical question, that is, if so and so were such and such, etc., what is your opinion. Incidentally, the hypothetical question cannot be used for any other but an expert witness. The hypothetical question is so broad and all-encompassing that it generally covers the entire direct testimony of the witness. He is then subject to the opposing lawyer's cross-examination which is covered by the usual rules of that phase of the law of evidence.

It is in the testimony of the expert witness and the phrasing of the hypothetical question that psychiatry and law are the furthest apart and in almost direct conflict. The law as especially exemplified by the trial judges insists that expert testimony be fitted on their legal theories which have been built up by centuries of common law decisions and precedents. The psychiatrist refuses to have his theories fitted to this Procrustean bed of legal precedents, and insists on using his own language and own theories to elucidate his opinion and that he be permitted to state grounds for his opinions in his language. Fortunately, the law is slowly changing in the psychiatrist's favor and he is being given greater leeway in testifying as to his opinion of the effects of psychiatry on the issue of competency in the case at bar.

When is a psychiatrist needed in a case to give an opinion as an expert witness? The answer is: Whenever the competency of some person in a case is placed in issue.

In a criminal case, it is primarily to determine whether the accused person had the necessary criminal intent to commit the crime for which he has been charged at the time he was alleged to have committed the crime. In the discussion of the substantive law of crime in Chapter 8 hereafter, it will be learned that a crime consists of an act together with a criminal intent, so that one of the crucial points that a public prosecutor must prove is this criminal intent, and a successful plea of insanity will always be a complete defense. But in a criminal trial, two points of time come under the province of the court in determining any issue of sanity that is raised, the time of the alleged crime, and the time when the alleged perpetrator thereof appears for trial. We have just discussed the insanity issue at the time the crime was committed. And at the time of the trial, the law frowns upon passing judgment upon a person who at that time is incompetent to defend himself. So a person can perform a criminal act with the necessary criminal intent and still go unpunished (not freed) if at the time of the trial it can be proved that he is incompetent. Note that in the Jack Ruby case, his attorneys are trying to prove him insane not only at the time he killed President Kennedy's assassin, but also at the time of his trial, and at present. Proof of any of these would serve to avert his execution, the latter two to postpone it until he regains sanity, the first to avert criminal sanctions completely in favor of psychiatric rehabilitation which if successful would then set him free.

In a civil case, there is only one relevant time, that at which the alleged incompetent executed his will, conveyance or otherwise, signed a contract, committed a tort or otherwise involved himself with others in a civil matter. At the time of trial, his competency is of no importance so long as he is adequately represented. His state of mind at the time of the trial or his death if the validity of his will is at issue is of importance only as possible evidence as to the state of his mind at the one relevant time as above defined.

One further point on incompetency must be noted. Though there are few cases on the subject, a witness is not disqualified as such by reason of insanity, imbecility, disease, intoxication or any other form of mental derangement unless his condition precludes trustworthiness in his powers of observation, recollection or narration. A witness's competency is presumed but can be disproved by expert testimony of a psychiatrist. A judgment of commitment on the other hand raises a presumption of incompetency.

Part III—INSANITY, SUBSTANTIVE LAW

Chapter 7

INCOMPETENT'S CONTRACTS

In considering the substantive law of the relations of potential incompetents (or patients as we have used this word) with other people, modified by their mental illness, the subject has been divided into contracts, torts and crimes and other relationships. Here contracts are considered.

The law has always eyed with disfavor a contract between a sane and insane person. It has been said that "a court of equity guards with jealous care all contracts with persons of unsound mind." 1/ The fundamental idea of a contract is that it requires the mutual assent of two parties. An insane person has nothing that the law recognizes as a mind. But whether a contract with an incompetent is void or voidable remains in doubt since judges and writers use these two words in different senses, and each case must be studied individually, depending on the facts in the case. Where a contract is wholly executory, that is, has not been performed by either party, so that neither party will be injured, there is a greater tendency to allow the incompetent to treat the contract as void or voidable. The earlier and now minority view is that a contract is void. But if the conclusion is that such a contract is void, it cannot be ratified, or in other words, the incompetent cannot enforce it if it turns out to be profitable to him, and innocent third party holders of personal property sold by an incompetent would not and could not acquire title, under the Uniform Sales Act.

In many instances, where the condition of the potential incompetent is not poor enough to enable him to avoid liability, the presence of other factors such as inadequacy of consideration, confidential relationship, fraud, duress, undue influence, etc. may enable the quasi-incompetent to invalidate the contract.

Statutory provisions relating to mental capacity are construed according to their language. The individual nature of each transaction can never be stressed too much, and it must be borne in mind that mental capacity to contract is determined with respect to the particular contract at issue and not to the transaction of business in general.

In some cases where the contract had been fully executed, there was no hardship on the incompetent and the other person was unaware of the incompetent's mental state, the incompetent has not been permitted to invalidate the contract. But as in most cases involving insanity, the degree of the affliction is most important, and where the incompetent is only ill to a minor degree, the courts are more likely to find him liable in connection with the other elements of the case than where his illness is so severe as to make him a non-functioning person in almost every sense of the term.

Necessities

There is a class of contracts which do bind an incompetent, even if a committee or guardian has been appointed for him, namely, where necessities have been furnished him. This is not because such a contract is valid, but rather it is an obligation in the nature of quasi-contract in order to protect the incompetent, so that he may be able to help himself in case of necessity. Following this line of reasoning, an executory contract to furnish necessities is still a void one, since necessities have not as yet been furnished to the incompetent, only promised. Also, if there is a formal contract under which necessities have been furnished, the incompetent is not bound by the contract price, but by the reasonable value of the services. As a matter of fact, because of the quasi-contractual nature of the obligation, that is, imposed by law because of the status of one of the parties, there is no necessity of a formal contract. Finally, the necessities must have been furnished on the credit or with the intent to charge the incompetent personally and not some one else. These rules apply as well to members of the incompetent's family whom he is under legal obligation to support. This doctrine of necessities includes money borrowed by an incompetent to the extent that it has been used to purchase necessities.

Just what constitutes necessities for an incompetent is a relative matter. It is whatever is reasonably necessary for the support, maintenance, care and comfort of the incompetent and his family according to the state and condition in life during the previous life of the incompetent before he became one. They are not limited to actual wants. When legal services are required, these are considered necessities, especially where criminal charges are involved, and under the law as outlined above, the incompetent is liable for legal services actually performed for him to the extent of their reasonable value, not the amount agreed upon. Also, under this doctrine of necessities, a person can become an involuntary agent of an incompetent, that is, the relationship is established by operation of law, but only to the extent necessary to furnish necessities.

Agency

The general rules of contract law discussed above apply in general and only exceptions or modifications are considered here. An incompetent is incapable of selecting an agent, and it must be pointed out that when a committee or guardian is appointed by the court, he does not become the incompetent's agent. But an incompetent may have an agent appointed for him by law, as for instance an attorney as described above on this page. There is the same confusion among courts and law writers as to whether a contract of agency with a lunatic is void or voidable, the tendency towards the former being stronger than in the case of an ordinary contract. However, in the case of a third party, unaware of the principal's incompetency, acting in good faith and giving consideration that is used for the benefit of the incompetent and who cannot be restored to his former position, the courts have tended to uphold the validity of the agency agreement. A principal to an agency contract must be of sound mind but an agent to an agency contract may be of less than sound mind, not even sui juris, provided he is above the degree of capability and intelligence of a lunatic or imbecile and can perform as agent in the particular case. An agency is ordinarily terminated by the insanity of a principal, whether legally so adjudicated or not, except as to an innocent third party unaware of such insanity or an agency coupled with an interest. However, where there has been no adjudication, the fact of insanity must be clear, notorious and of a type that affects the principal's exercise of his will. The insanity of an agent terminates the agency as a matter of law. As indicated above, the time of insanity is generally at the time of adjudication, but may be prior depending on the circumstances of the case.

Negotiable Instruments

Since the law of Negotiable Instruments or Bills and Notes as it is sometimes called is a separate and distinct branch of the law, codified as the Uniform Negotiable Instruments Law in all the states of the union, the question of insanity in connection with a negotiable instrument must be studied in the context of that law. A maker of a negotiable instrument must be of sound mind or else the instrument is void. The test here is competency to know and understand the transaction. The social conflict here is between the need to protect incompetents on the one hand and innocent holders of commercial paper on the other. The courts have generally decided for the former and hold that a negotiable instrument made or indorsed by an insane person is void as against a holder in due course, ruling that the latter takes the bill or note with implied knowledge of the mental capacity of the previous parties. Here again we come into the previously discussed conflict of void and voidable. If the particular jurisdiction or rather particular case holds that the making or indorsing of a negotiable instrument by an incompetent is void, it cannot be enforced by a holder in due course against such incompetent. On the other hand, if it holds it voidable, it is no defense against a holder in due course prior to knowledge of incompetency, except in the case of an incompetent accommodation endorser who of course has received no consideration for his endorsement.

Footnotes

1/Parrish v. People 214 Minn. 580, 9 N.W.2 225

Chapter 8

INCOMPETENT'S WRONGFUL ACTS

The wrongful acts of an incompetent are of two kinds: Those affecting only other persons or civil wrongs, called torts; and those affecting the state or public welfare as well as other persons or criminal wrongs, called crimes.

Torts

Of all the fields of substantive law affected by the mental competence of a person involved, the law of torts is the simplest and easiest to outline. Unlike the other branches of law, insanity in the law of torts has little effect on deciding the liability or non-liability of an incompetent, and in most cases save for a few minor differences, the insanity of a party in an action in torts makes no difference. The general rule is that an insane party is liable for his own torts, unless the particular tort involves a specific intention which he is incapable of entertaining, such as some libels and slanders. The fact that the person complaining of the tort knew of the wrongdoer's insanity and might have prevented the act makes no difference. Nor is there a distinction between nonfeasance and misfeasance and the incompetent is held to the same degree of care and diligence as a person of sound mind. The reasoning behind these cases is again of a quasi-social rather than a strictly legal nature. Again the law is confronted with the question of placing the burden of loss on one of two innocent persons, the incompetent who by definition is unable to take care of himself and the injured party who has suffered damage. Here, unlike the law of negotiable instruments discussed above in Chapter 7 at page 80, the burden is placed on the incompetent as the person best able to bear it.

However, an incompetent person is not liable for damages caused to another where that person, by his own wrongful act, caused the temporary insanity or unconsciousness under which the insane person acted. This is a special rule governing the torts of insane persons, but it would also seem to be an example of contributory negligence under which doctrine any injured plaintiff cannot recover from any defendant where he himself has been negligent.

In the case of a libel or slander, an incompetent is not liable if intent or malice was an element of the tort and he can prove total derangement or delusions concerning the subject of his defamatory words. If not in such serious mental condition, he can prove the state of his sanity as mitigation of damages or as limiting his liability to actual or compensatory damages. Any degree of insanity is a defense against exemplary or punitive damages even where there is a statute permitting them against a sane defendant.

Coming back to the question of contributory negligence, there are two schools of thought on negligence itself, the objective that the standard of care be the same for everybody and the subjective that the standard of care be tailored to the actual failings and shortcomings of the alleged tortfeasor. One expert on torts, Professor Fleming James Jr. of Yale Law School has taken a position squarely on the fence, 1/ objective for the defendant on the question of the defendant's negligence and subjective on the question of the plaintiff's contributory negligence. However, anomalous this may seem, it is a fact that most courts seem to be lenient towards plaintiffs whose mental capacity is only subnormal, that is, a subjective standard is adopted.

The liability of an incompetent for torts of others acting in his behalf depends on the nature of the acts and circumstances that caused the injury. This depends to a certain extent on the law of agency. As we have seen previously, Chapter 7, page 79, a committee or guardian is not the agent of his ward. This is because he acquires his authority to act from the court that appointed him, unlike the agent who dervies his from his principal. Nonetheless, there are elements of a quasi-agency in the relationship. On the sub-

83

ject of injuries caused by the negligent maintenance of the ward's property by the committee, some courts hold the incompetent innocent of such wrongdoing. However, others hold him liable as owner of the premises although not himself negligent. This rule of his liability holds true in the negligent operation of an elevator owned by the incompetent, as an incident of the ownership of property. Apparently the court held him liable as an implied principal, despite the general rule that insanity voids a contract of agency. On the negligent operation of an automobile owned but not under his control, the incompetent is not liable. But he is liable where the driver is under his control.

Finally, the custodian of an insane person is not liable for his torts, as covered previously, but he may be liable where he fails to take reasonable care under the circumstances.

Crimes

Although this is only the penultimate chapter in this book, in a sense we reach its climax when we approach the law of insanity as it affects criminal law. For insanity in criminal proceedings is the most interesting, most dramatic and most publicized portion of the law of insanity. One has only to look at our daily newspapers for one week to encounter cases of homicide with overtones of insanity. Then also, greatly publicized cases like the Clutter family in the midwest, the subject of Truman Capote's "In Cold Blood," the murder of Lee Oswald, the assassin of President Kennedy, by Jack Ruby, and the recent multiple murders by Richard Speck in Chicago and Charles Whitman in Austin. There is tremendous public interest in cases like these which is catered to beyond the point of satiety by the many and varied types of media. Finally hundreds of novels, plays, stories, movies and TV programs are based on this combination of murder and insanity, including such great plays as Aeschuylus' "Oresteia," Sophocles' "Oedipus Rex" and Shakespeare's "Hamlet," "Macbeth," "King Lear" and "Othello." It is probably not an exaggeration to say that, to the ordinary person, the term law refs to homicide with the element of insanity.

At common law and in some jurisdictions which have abandoned the criminal law in favor of a statutory criminal code, 2/ an accused criminal who becomes insane after the commission of the crime cannot be tried for the crime or required to plead while he remains insane. Likewise, if he becomes insane during the trial, it must be abated. In such cases, the accused criminal is committed to a mental hospital until he recovers his sanity in which case the proceedings are continued at the point of interruption caused by the defendant's insanity.

An accused criminal who has been acquitted on the defense of insanity is usually committed to a state institute for the criminal insane where he remains until recovery. When sanity has been recovered, the patient is entitled to his freedom and must be discharged.

The rules of the substantive law of insanity are fairly well defined, with several exceptions which will be noted when we come to them. The problem, essentially true of all branches of Anglo-American law but especially here, is that of fitting the rules to the facts of the particular case. "Sui generis," the only one of its kind, must be the motto emblazoned on the banners of he who would probe the mysteries of the law of criminal insanity.

There must be both act and criminal intent (or mens rea) to constitute a crime, and therefore no one can be held responsible for, or guilty of, a crime unless he has sufficient mental capacity. Amnesia alone is not a defense to a crime, unless it can be proven that the amnesia caused the defendant to be unable to know the nature and quality and wrongness of his action. On the other hand, unconsciousness is generally a defense to a criminal prosecution, with some modification to be discussed hereinafter. Therefore, a person suffering insanity of the necessary kind or degree at the time of the commission of the crime has a complete defense, and a statute providing otherwise would probably be unconstitutional. It must be a type pertinent to the crime committed and therefore an adjudication of insanity and commitment to a mental hospital is not conclusive but merely evidence of insanity. The mental illness necessary to provide a defense must be such as to render the defendant incapable of knowing what he is doing or to know right from wrong or to rob him of volition so that he is controlled by insane and irresistible impulse. Merely allowing one's emotions to get out of control or a fit of "temporary insanity" during a quarrel brought on by the defendant does not constitute the degree of insanity necessary to a complete defense. On the other hand, idiots, imbeciles, lunatics, feebleminded persons, kleptomaniacs (limited to stealing and results thereof) and paranoics are all in a class whose mental illness excuses them from the legal consequences of otherwise criminal acts. But so-called hereditary insanity is only evidence of complete insanity, not a defense by itself. The time of the commission of the crime is essential and even if the accused was insane prior to and immediately after the crime, this is no defense if it can be proven that he was sane or had a lucid interval at the moment of committing the crime.

We come now to the degree of capacity and tests of responsibility in general, and with the criteria established by the famous M'Naghten 3/ and Durham 4/ cases. The law of insanity is not a world of black and white, but a vast grayness, of all degrees of gray, shading imperceptibly but not uniformly from black to white. The issue is not merely insanity but insanity as a conclusive defense to a criminal charge, and a slight case of insanity may exonerate the defendant whereas, as pointed out above, page 85, insanity sufficiently great to warrant hospitalization is not per se a conclusive defense. Also, although not a conclusive defense, insanity may serve to mitigate the charge.

The most important case in setting the test of responsibility in criminal-insanity trials in Anglo-American law for the past century and a quarter has been M'Naghten's case, previously cited. M'Naghten, a paranoic also suffering from delusions was convinced that he was being persecuted by Sir Robert Peel, England's Conservative Prime Minister. Mistaking Sir Robert's secretary for the P.M., he murdered the former and was acquitted of his crime on the defense of insanity. All classes of Victorian society were shocked at the outcome and little assuaged by the monarch's remark that she "did not believe that anyone could be insane who wanted to murder a Conservative Prime Minister".5/ The outcry was such that the House of Lords felt compelled to submit certain questions to the judges of England for clarification of the law of insanity. The judges after lengthy discussion concluded that to establish a defense on the ground of insanity, it must be clearly proved that, at the time of the committing of the crime, the accused was of such degree of mental illness that he did not know the nature and quality of the act he was doing or that if he did know, he was unaware that he was doing what was wrong. This criterion, the so-called right-wrong test, far from clarifying the law, made it more confusing and uncertain and became the target, beginning about a century ago of sharp criticism by legal scholars and psychiatrists.

Finally, a new criterion was established by Circuit Judge David L. Bazelon in the Durham case cited above. Judge Bazelon, a legal scholar on the subject of criminal insanity, exhaustively examined the law on the subject since the M'Naghten case and found it inconclusive, misleading and in sharp variance with the conclusion of the science of psychiatry. The judgment of guilty in the lower court was reversed and a new criterion was established for the lower court to follow in a retrial of the case. The new criterion "is simply that an accused is not criminally responsible if his unlawful act was the product of mental disease or mental defect" $214F_2$ at p. 874. Disease is defined as a condition capable of improving or deteriorating; defect as a condition incapable of change which may be congenital, traumatic or the residual effect of a physical or mental disease. The jury, as the ultimate trier of the facts, must be provided with two guides; one, if the jury believes beyond a reasonable doubt that the accused was not suffering from a mental disease or defect at the time of the crime, he may be found guilty; two, if he was suffering from a mental disease or defect at the time of the crime and the jury believes beyond a reasonable doubt that the act was not a product of such mental abnormality, he may be found guilty. But if these two tests are not met, he **must** be found not guilty. However, the old right-wrong test still remains, giving an accused another means of defense. However, even the Durham rule does not obliterate the distinction between legal insanity and psychiatric insanity, and it is the former, as defined by statute and case law in legal terms, that governs.

Parenthetically, it may be observed that right at this point is the core of the problem. When the legislatures and courts attempt to solve a problem concerning scientific facts, attested and proven by a body of science, psychiatry, in terms differing from the conclusions of that science but using the same terminology, there is bound to be confusion and indecision. While law, as a so-called social science, contains moral values and judgments that are absent from psychiatry, it must at least take its leadership from psychiatry and not attempt to establish its own body of learning as a pseudopsychiatry. When the law learns to respect psychiatry and to follow its leadership save where it conflicts with law's moral qualities, the problems of legal insanity will be considerably simplified.

Originally it had been intended to indicate the rules and precedents concerning the law of criminal insanity in every American jurisdiction. But the complex nature of the subject, the individuality (sui generis) of each case and the rapid changes in the law since Durham would have necessitated a volume twice this size. Where generalizations have been made, they were taken from legal articles on the subject.

There are certain areas of disagreement which will be discussed now. Insane delusions or partial insanity arising from a diseased mind afford a defense where the imagined facts would have afforded a justification if real. This is the rule in every jurisdiction in which the issue has arisen. However, where the imagined facts do not justify the commission of the act even if real, the courts split, some holding that the delusions or partial insanity afford a complete defense, others that they do not. Of course, in any event, the insane delusion must be connected with the crime. The courts in coming to their differing conclusions seem to place great reliance on the right and wrong test of the M'Naghten Rule, discussed previously. With the new outlook of the Durham case, it is quite likely that any delusion of an insane person that is connected with the crime committed will serve as a complete defense.

There is a similar conflict of authority concerning a crime committed in a condition of irresistible impulse where the accused knows the nature and quality of his act and its wrongness, but is unable to restrain himself. The majority, following the M'Naghten rule, hold it to be no defense, but a minority, emphasizing the accused's mental illness, declare it to be a complete defense. The term "irresistible impulse" is a poor one seeming to connote a sudden, spontaneous feeling, but it is the best language to date. Even the minority do not conceive of a paroxysm of rage as an excuse for murder, but insist on a background of slowly developing insanity culminating in volitional incapacity. In some cases, the courts feel compelled to accept the majority doctrine by specific statutory language or a statutory definition of insanity that excludes an irresistible impulse from the definition of insanity.

Kleptomania presents a peculiar application of the "irresistible impulse" rules. It is defined as an irrestible desire to steal which weakens the will power to such an extent to render the victim of it powerless to control himself, and is usually a complete and valid defense to the crime of larceny. Yet on the other hand, some courts hold it to be of no avail, following the M'Naghten Rule right-wrong test.

Anger and emotional insanity as a defense to a crime is tolerated even less than irresistible impulse. Even in the minority jurisdictions discussed above, mainly those following the Durham Rule, that recognize volitional incapacity, mere anger or strong emotion will not be permitted as a defense. But where the emotional insanity is an overwhelming passion of some duration in time, the courts will find a complete derangement of the intellect which serves as a defense to the crime.

There is a similar conflict over so called moral insanity, the M'Naghten jurisdictions holding it to be no defense no matter how depraved the accused may be. But in some states where volitional incapacity is recognized, where the moral insanity goes beyond mere depravity or perversion of moral values into mental disease where the defendant, while knowing right and wrong, cannot control his will power, the courts will exonerate him on this ground.

Intoxication

Intoxication is not limited to that caused by alcohol, but includes effects from drugs, and in this subdivision, hypnotic trances. Generally, at common law and under most criminal statutes, voluntary intoxication is no defense to a crime committed while thus intoxicated especially where there is neither purpose, motive nor intent as an element of the particular crime involved.6/ Since alcholic intoxication is an act of moral wrongdoing so charged with danger to others, the fact that the alcoholic is unconscious of what he is doing or cannot distinguish between right and wrong is no defense to a criminal prosecution absent the element of specific intent as part of the crime involved. However, drunkenness may be considered in determinining whether the crime was accidental and excusable. Somnambulism, considered as an involuntary intoxication which temporarily destroys the moral agency so that the sleep walker comes under the right-wrong test, is usually a complete defense to a crime. However, if it is artificially induced by the defendant by wilful drinking, there is no excuse. Likewise there is no exoneration for intoxication to a person who by constitutional infirmity or traumatic incident is unusually susceptible to alcohol or to a person whose voluntary intoxication creates delusions under whose influence the crime is committed.

Voluntary intoxication serves neither to aggravate nor mitigate the crime committed but it sometimes mitigates the punishment.

Where a particular purpose, motive or intent is an element of the crime involved and the accused's voluntary intoxication makes it impossible for him to entertain this mental element of the crime, this is usually7/ a complete defense. This majority rule is applied cautiously, and is not a defense where the necessary mental capacity or mens rea is present prior to the intoxication and the accused then drinks himself into a state of insobriety prior to committing the crime. Mere intoxication alone is not sufficient as a defense; there must be such a degree of drunkenness as to suspend the power of reason and in effect to come under the right-wrong rule.

Involuntary intoxication, where the accused becomes drunk, not under his own volition but under the instigation of another by means of force, fraud, duress, stratagem, etc., is a complete defense to a criminal charge. Again, this is a rule applied with caution. The volition of the accused must be destroyed and his drinking must be entirely involuntary. A voluntary, social kind of drinking to the point of intoxication followed by instigation to a deeper level by some one for the purpose of inducing the defendant to commit a crime which he then does is no excuse.

Where drinking brings on a temporary insanity of the type of a mental excitement or frenzy, this does not excuse the drinker. But where it brings on delirium tremens or deprives the drinker of moral judgment to distinguish right from wrong, the drunkard has a complete defense. Again, we come to a variation of the right-wrong rule of M'Naghten's case. Questions of whether there is such a disease as dipsomania whether defendant had it at the time of the crime and whether the crime was a product of that disease are all questions for the jury.8/Again we find the ridiculous situation of twelve lay persons being called on, not only to apply part of the science of psychiatry, but to define it.

An insane person's immunity from criminal prosecution by reason of his mental illness is not changed by his voluntary intoxication the excitement from which may increase his infirmity. The defense is still based on his mental illness and not on his state of intoxication.

Drugs

The rules as to drug taking are similar to those involving alcoholic intoxication. Mere voluntary drug taking yields no excuse unless the drug taker has reached a state of so-called permanent insanity that destroys moral judgment. Addiction to the point of involuntary usage of the drug constitutes such permanent insanity. The right-wrong criterion again is the one used.

The current craze for LSD makes this portion of the law of criminal insanity of great moment. Since many LSD "flights" render the user temporarily insane, it seems that it should be a defense, but since it is a morally wrongful act and the insanity is not of a permanent type, the M'-Naghten jurisdiction probably will hold the defendant guilty. The influence of the Durham case will probably work to the contrary. There are no known reported cases on the subject.

Where drug usage proceeds to the point of insanity, there is a complete defense but this is under the general rules of insanity rather than the similar statutes or decisions relating to alcoholism. Insanity caused by drugs administered as medicine by a licensed physician (iatrogenic psychosis) or by means of fraud constitutes a valid defense.

Hypnotism

If it can be proved that the defendant committed the alleged crime while under the influence of "hypnotism," this would undoubtedly be a complete valid defense. Hypnotism has been defined as a peculiar physiological condition excited by perverted action of certain parts of the cerebral nervous system, in which the subject acts in obedience to the will of the operator, so that he did not know what he was doing, or was compelled to commit the crime. But mere testimony that another told the defendant to commit the crime is not sufficient; there must be evidence of the overwhelming of the defendant's will power by the hypnotist's machinations.

Conclusion

Criminal law has always had extralegal aspects from its very beginnings, political, in the derogatory sense of the word, and sociological.

When at the dawn of civilization, polities were rising up out of primitive savage fury, they were usually led by one or several leaders or heroes who established their groups in safe places where they were at peace to develop their economy and society. All mythologies contain stories of these kinds and even the sophisticated Plutarch repeats them in his biographies of the founders of Athens and Rome. And when the leader-heroes grew old and questions of their successors arose, few were averse to perverting the legitimate criminal law to the execution or imprisonment of rivals, dissidents or other troublemakers. This same perverting phenomenon exists today in our dictatorships, whether regarded as good or evil.

And as the criminal law developed to protect the members of the polity from internal enemies, social questions constantly arose. What was the purpose of a criminal code: retaliation, retribution in bloody fashion by the polity on behalf of the wronged to avoid greater and more savage criminal acts? Was it rehabilitation or corrective treatment, to make the outlaw once again a useful citizen or to use him as another and expendable bulwark against the polity's outside enemies? Or was there a higher social purpose present in the attempt to prevent future crime, the regard by the citizens of a criminal as an "accursed of God" punished enough by the devil within him that committed the crime.

Nor are these differing concepts of primitive criminology easy to recognize and categorize. The "lex talionis" of the Old Testament is usually thought of as a law of revenge, but rather it may be a law of limitation. Thus, "an eye for an eye" may not be as bloody as it sounds; it is not that thou suffering the loss of an eye shall be compensated by the loss of thine enemy's eye—rather it is that thou in thy loss shall be limited in the vengeance to no more than thou lost.

However, there can be no doubt that criminal law, pen-

93

ology, criminology and the law and criminal insanity had their origins in the dim mists of the dawn of civilization, far antedating the most ancient of ancient civilizations. Here the student of criminal insanity turns to archeology, anthropology, zoology, mythology, paleontology and similar sciences of ancient lore which, at first blush, have very little in common with the suave, sophisticated modernity of today's law courts and the urbane justices, attorneys and psychiatrists who elucidate it today.

Law, as with every other so-called social science, is dynamic in its essence, presenting a different aspect to the world at different periods of civilization and culture, but few are changing with the rapidity and earth shaking consequences as is the law of criminal insanity. Not only the Durham case but new discoveries in psychiatry, physiology and other branches of medicine, new statutes of great social import, new concepts, etc. are changing the entire picture of criminal law and jurisprudence as well as the insanity portions thereof. While difficult to delineate in detail, the broad picture is clear. Slowly but steadily the social concept of rehabilitation is forging ahead of the legal concept of punishment, and the lot of the criminally insane becomes easier as it becomes better understood.

Footnotes

1/ 63 Harvard Law Review 769 @ p. 782.

2/ United States, Alabama, Arizona, Arkansas, California, Colorado, District of Columbia, Florida, Georgia, Illinois, Iowa, Kansas, Kentucky, Louisiana, Maryland, Massachusetts, Mississippi, New Jersey, New Mexico, New York, Ohio, Oklahoma, Pennsylvania, Rhode Island, Tennessee, Texas, Vermont, Washington, West Virginia and Wisconsin. Louisiana was never a common law state, deriving its law, not from England, but from the Code Napoleon. However, its statute on this subject is similar to those of her sister states.

3/ Daniel M'Naghten's Case, 10 C&F 200, 8 Eng. Reports 718 (1843).

4/ Durham v. United States F2862 (1954).

5/ Quoted in Sheldon Glueck, "Law and Psychiatry," page 44.

6/ United States, Alabama, Arizona, California, Colorado, Delaware, District of Columbia, Florida, Georgia, Illinois, Iowa, Kentucky, Maine, Maryland, Massachusetts, Michigan, Mississippi, Missouri, Nebraska, Nevada, New Jersey, North Carolina, Ohio, Oklahoma, Pennsylvania, Rhode Island, Tennessee, Texas, Utah, Virginia and Washington. New York as to misdemeanors.

7/ Missouri contra, 354 Mo. 265.

8/ State v. Pike 49 N.H. 399, the historic case setting forth the New Hampshire rule which was relied on by Judge Bazelon in the Durham Case supra.

Chapter 9

OTHER LEGAL RESULTS OF INSANITY

This is in effect a catch-all or miscellaneous chapter covering all other legal relations of an incompetent not previously discussed. These generally are in the nature of the status of the incompetent and his rights and disabilities arising out of his mental illness, in contrast to his contractual relationships and wrongful conduct previously considered.

Marriages and Divorce

At common law, and in some states where the rules concerning marriage have been codified, a marriage to a person without mental capacity is void. It is therefore subject to collateral attack, will be declared invalid in any court and in any proceeding in which the question may arise whether ,during the life of the parties or after the death of either or both of them and a decree of nullification is not required in order to establish the invalidity of the marriage, although the granting of such a decree is proper.

However, in other states, usually as a result of a statute, such a marriage is voidable only and therefore cannot be attacked collaterally or impeached after the death of either party and is valid until set aside in a proper proceeding for that purpose. The marriage can be set aside by either party provided the sane one did not know of the other's mental illness prior to the marriage.

The degree of capacity required to marry and the particular classes of mental disease that incapacitate a marriage are of a myriad variety and must be carefully distinguished, generally on the test of the ability to understand the special nature of the marriage contract and the duties and responsbilities entailed by it. A person suffering from paranoia, delirium tremens or feeble-mindedness is usually incompetent to marry. Not every form of insanity incapacitates a marriage. Mere feeblemindedness, great eccentricity or singularity of conduct, mental dejection, the propensity to some vice or uncontrollable impulse and partial dementia are not sufficient to invalidate a marriage. Similarly as to kleptomania and epilepsy, though a statute may disqualify the latter from marriage. Usually the test in the validity of a marriage contract is the same degree of mental sufficiency to enter an ordinary contract.

The relevant time element is the precise time of the marriage and insane periods before or after the marriage do not affect it save as evidence of insanity at the time of the marriage. No matter how deep the mental illness, if there was a lucid interval at the time of the marriage, it is a valid one.

Severe intoxication sufficient to deprive the drinker of his reason invalidates the marriage. It is usually held that such a marriage is voidable, and may be set aside by the drunken party, at least prior to the consummation of the marriage.

The appointment of a committee or guardian of an incompetent of one of the pair or the commitment of one to a mental hospital is not sufficient per se to invalidate a marriage, provided it is proved that the incompetent has the mental capacity otherwise to contract a marriage.

The manner of terminating the marriage on the ground of prenuptial insanity depends on the jurisdiction as previously elucidated. Where a marriage is void as at common law, annulment is the proper remedy, not divorce. Where the common law has been replaced by statute which codifies the common law rule, again the remedy is the same. Where the statute states that such insanity is a ground for divorce, the remedy is divorce. Table A in the Appendix indicates which states permit the dissolution of a marriage entered into by an incompetent and on what ground. However, it must be added that the law so abhors a marital union contracted between a sane and insane person that the court will effect a dissolution in one way or another unless the statutes specifically outlaw it, in which case the constitutionality of such a statute would be questionable.

Where insanity arises after marriage, the common law did not recognize this as a ground for dissolution of the marriage so the only relief possible in such a situation is whatever the statutes provide. Some statutes permit this unrestrictedly as a ground of divorce, while others hedge it around with restrictions such as a stay in a mental hospital for a stated period or a formal commitment or both. Table A in the Appendix indicates the statutory grounds and restrictions for a divorce on the ground of insanity.

Where insanity is not a ground for divorce and a suit for divorce on one of the statutory grounds specified has been commenced, the insanity of the defendant, if it was the proximate cause of the matrimonial wrong complained of, is a valid defense.

Property Rights

An insane person may acquire property by inheritance or deed unless a burden or obligation is placed on him, and he still may do so even when he is a ward of a court as a result of an appointment of a committee or guardian. Title is in the name of the incompetent, not of the committee. Where no committee has been appointed, the acts of the incompetent in respect to such property are voidable, not void.

Wills

At common law, there was no right or privilege to dispose of one's property after death. Whatever rights do exist are by reason of statutory enactment. However, where in most instances statutes which are in derogation of the common law are strictly construed, the various Statutes of Wills of the different jurisdictions are very liberally construed. Here we are concerned only with the testator's mental capacity to make a will. This is a requirement in every statutory scheme permitting the descent of property by will, since as we have previously seen, the law deems an insane person to be unable to effectuate any legal transaction. The time of the necessary mental capacity is the period or time of the execution of the will.

The rules for determining mental capacity of a testator seem to be the most lenient of all, so intent are the courts to give effect to a testator's last expressed wishes. In general, a testator must have a mentality and memory sufficient to understand the transaction of making a will, to comprehend generally the nature of the property to be devised, to recollect the natural objects of his bounty and to understand what the will purports to effect. Disappointing of some legitimate claims does not negate testamentary capacity. Understanding of the ordinary facts of life is sufficient; he need not have perfect understanding nor make a wise disposition of his property to sustain his mental capacity. No particular degree of mentality is required and each case must be determined on its own facts. Neither a high order of intelligence nor an absolutely sound mind is required. Even mental weakness does not disqualify a testator, but he may be adjudicated to lack testamentary capacity without being insane. Less mental capacity is required to make a will than for carrying on business transactions and anyone capable of doing the latter is **ipso facto** competent to make a will. But a will executed under the influence of insanity or an insane delusion in the legal not the medical sense is invalid, provided the insanity or insane delusion has a direct bearing on the testamentary act. Adjudication of insanity or inability to handle one's affairs, commitment to a mental hospital or appointment of a guardian or committee do not establish testator's lack of testamentary capacity.

As above stated under property rights, a devisee or legatee need not have any mental capacity to receive a gift under a will.

Gifts

The maxim **nemo est haerens viventis** no one is the heir of a living person would seem to indicate that there are no restrictions upon the right of a property owner to give away his property to whomever or in whatever amounts he desires. On the other hand, the law, probably due to some vestigial remainder of the feudal system, insists that a person cannot give away his property during his lifetime unless he is mentally competent. The tests vary. Some states say the criterion is the same low standard as applies to testamentary capacity. Others insist on the capacity to contract, while still others take as in-between stance, setting the test as capacity of the donor to understand the nature and consequences of his gift, which is lower than the capacity to transact business generally. The crucial time is the time of making the gift and prior or later incapacity is of no moment.

Like a legatee, a donee needs no degree of mental capacity in order to have the gift vest in him.

Deeds

One who executes a deed passing title to property must have proper mental capacity to do so. The test here is the capacity to understand the nature of the act and its consequence. The significant time here is at two periods: the signing of the contract and of the deed. As with other transactions heretofore the facts in each case must govern. Total insanity isn't required to void the transaction, merely inability to understand it. On the other hand, old age and weakness alone do not establish incompetence; again we go back to the test of understanding.

But if the grantor has already been adjudicated an incompetent or had a committee appointed, the deed is void or voidable depending on the jurisdiction.

BIBLIOGRAPHY

Alexander, Franz G. M.D. & Selesnick, Shelton T. M.D. The History of Psychiatry, New York 1966

Arieti, Silvano, Ed. "American Handbook of Psychiatry" Vols. I & II New York 1959

Bluemel, C. S. M.D. "Psychiatry and Common Sense" New York 1954

Dunbar, Flanders M.D. "Mind and Body" New York 1955

Fromm-Reichman, Frieda "Psychoanalysis and Psychotherapy, Selected Papers" Chicago 1959

Harper & James "The Law of Torts" Boston 1956

Holmes, Oliver Wendell Jr. "The Common Law" Boston 1881, Cambridge 1963

Langner, Thomas S. & Michael, Stanley T. "Life Stress and Mental Health" New York 1963

Monroe, Ruth L. "Schools of Psychoanalytic Thought" New York 1955

Overholser, Winfred M.D. "The Psychiatrist and the Law" New York 1953

Rose, Arnold M. Ed. "Mental Health and Mental Disorder, a Sociological Approach" New York 1955

Special Committee to Study Commitment Procedures of the Bar Ass'n of the City of New York—Mental Illness and Due Process Itahaca, N.Y. 1962

Strecker, Edward A. "Basic Psychiatry" New York 1952

Williston "The Law of Contracts" 3rd Ed. New York 1959

Williston "The Law of Sales" 2nd Ed. New York 1948

Wolberg, Lewis R. M.D. "The Technique of Psychotherapy" New York 1954

Zilboorg, Gregory M.D. "A History of Medical Psychology" New York 1954

GLOSSARY OF PSYCHIATRIC TERMINOLOGY

Unless otherwise indicated, this glossary is based upon Hinsie & Campbell's "Psychiatric Dictionary." Well known words or those defined in the text itself are omitted. The latter may be found by consulting the index.

ABREACTION.—The process of bringing to consciousness and, thus, to adequate expression, of material which has been unconscious (usually because of repression). Abreaction refers to the two aspects of a "complex"—the intellectual representation and the accompanying affect—and includes not only the recollection of forgotten memories and experiences but also their reliving with appropriate emotional display and discharge of affect. The method used to bring the repressed material into consciousness is called *catharsis* (q. v.); the term abreaction technically refers to the end-result.

The term "abreaction of emotion" refers to the discharge of emotion in the course of psychotherapy. This process is usually facilitated by the patient's gaining awareness of the causal relationship between the previously undischarged emotion and his symptoms. When such a discharge of emotion occurs during psychotherapy, it is often possible for the patient to see the link between the previously undischarged emotion and his symptoms. When such a discharge of emotion occurs during psychotherapy, it is often possible for the patient to see the link between his current irrational behavior and his demands toward his therapist, as well as the forgotten earlier counterpart from which the emotional attitude originated. The patient is thereby enabled to modify his anarchronistic, immature, incongruous, and unreal emotional demands in favor of more adequate and appropriate behavior.

AFFECT.—The feeling-tone accompaniment of an idea or mental representation. The affects are the most direct psychic derivatives of the instincts and are psychic representatives of the various bodily changes by means of which instincts manifest themselves. The affects regularly attach themselves to ideas and other psychic formations to which they did not originally belong, and as a result their origin and meaning remain hidden from consciousness. The affect itself may thus be conscious although it is typically displaced onto an idea to which it did not originally belong, and the original idea is unconscious. If an affect is completely suppressed, it may appear not as an emotion but rather as physical changes of innervations, such as perspiration, tachycardia, paresthesia, etc. In other cases, especially in catatonic and manic states, the affects may appear without disguise.

The term affect is also used, more loosely, as a class name for feeling, emotion, or mood.

AMBIVALENCE.—Bipolarity; the co-existence of antithetic emotions, attitudes, ideas, or wishes toward a given object or situation. The term was coined by Bleuler, who differentiated between affective or emotional ambivalence, intellectual ambivalence, and ambivalence of the will. In current usage, the term ambivalence without further qualification ordinarily refers to affective ambivalence.

Ambivalence is characteristic of the unconscious and of children. Its overt appearance in the adult implies the presence of definite pathology, such as obsessive-compulsive psychoneurosis, manic-depressive psychosis, or schizophrenia.

Ambivalence is one of the fundamental symptoms of schizophrenia (Bleuler), and here it may appear ·in any one or more of its three forms. In affective ambivalence, the very same concept is accompanied simultaneously by pleasant and unpleasant feelings. In ambivalence of the will, the desire to do a certain thing is accompanied by a desire not to do that thing. In ambivalence of the intellect, an idea appears simultaneously with the counter-idea.

Ambivalence persists normally in some degree throughout life, but even in late childhood it is markedly reduced in comparison to the age period of 2 to 5 years, and in the adult it typically appears in one part in consciousness while the antithetic feeling or idea or goal remains unconscious.

ANALGESIA.—Loss of the sense of pain. Analgesia may be of somatic or of psychic origin. It possesses psychiatric significance particularly in conversion hysteria, although the term is not as often seen today as it was in former years. Analgesia may be experimentally induced by hypnosis. Diminution of the sense of pain is not uncommon in advanced states of schizophrenia; its meaning in the latter condition is undetermined.

Analgesia refers to the absence of pain sensation brought about by some endogenous cause. Absence of pain sensation may also be induced by an exogenous agent, usually called an anodyne.

APRAXIA.—A disorder of voluntary movement in which the patient is more or less completely incapacitated to carry out purposeful movements, in spite of the absence of paralysis or other motor of sensory impairment.

AUTO-HYPNOSIS.—Auto-hypnosis is self-hypnosis. In one of Freud's early communications (on the *Psychical Mechanism of Hysterical Phenomena*, 1893), he emphasized the need on the part of the patient not only to remember the painful experience, but to live out its effect at the same time. He called this abreaction. Some patients are able to abreact on occasion when under the influence of auto hypnosis.

BLOCKAGE.—Horney's substitute conception for Freud's resistance. (Author's definition.) Blockages are all those forces which retard analysis and of which the patient may be unaware, particularly early in analysis. They are the patient's defenses. Harold Kelman in *American Handbook of Psychiatry.* P 1448.

BLOCKING.—Interruption of a trend of associative thought by the arousal of a countertrend or through the welling up into consciousness of a complex of unpleasant ideas. Webster Unabridged Dictionary, 3rd Ed.

CATHARSIS.—In psychiatry the term was first used by Freud to designate a type of psychotherapy. He tried through the methods of "free-association" and hypnosis to bring so-called traumatic experiences and their effective associations into consciousness. Psychiatric symptoms or symbols are looked upon as disguised representations of forgotten and repressed ideas or experiences. When the latter are

102

brought back into the sphere of consciousness and lived out fully (in a therapeutic sense), the method is called catharsis.

CATHEXIS.—Concentration of psychic energy upon a given object. Jones defines it as charge of energy; investment (of an idea) with feeling and significance. It is believed, for instance, that anxiety arises in relation to over-development of a libidinal cathexis.

CEREBROVASCULAR ACCIDENT.—Apoplexy; stroke. Cerebrovascular accidents include those conditions in which gross cerebral damage, hemorrhage, or softening follow a group of acute vascular disorders—cerebral thrombosis (82%), cerebral hemorrhage (15%), and cerebral embolism (3%).

Cerebral thrombosis is commonly a manifestation of cerebral arteriosclerosis and occurs in that age group, although children with an acute infectious disease and young syphilitic adults may also develop cerebral thrombosis.

Cerebral hemorrhage may occur suddenly, without warning, as a true "stroke." It occurs most commonly as a result of arteriosclerosis or hypertension, in the middle and older age groups.

Cerebral embolism creates the same clinical picture as cerebral thrombosis; but emboli are usually multiple and the syndrome may be more bizarre.

CHOREA.—A disorder characterized by irregular, spasmodic, involuntary movements of the limbs or facial muscles. Without a modifying word it usually means Sydenham's chorea or St. Vitus' dance.

COMPLEX.—A group of repressed ideas inter-linked into a complex whole, which besets the individual, impelling him to think, feel, and perhaps act after a habitual pattern. Jung, who introduced the term *complex* to psychiatry, describes it as the grouping "of physic elements about emotionally-toned contents." He adds that it "consists of a nuclear element and a great number of secondarily constellated associations." Apparently the contents of a complex may be in consciousness or in the unconscious. It is believed that the nuclear component is always in the unconscious. Jones defines a complex as "a group of emotionally invested ideas partially or entirely repressed."

MacCurdy defines a complex as "a group of ideas constellated by an instinctive process. The ideas are linked together, because they form a chain in some potential instinctive reaction. A complex is always unconscious, or at least, owes its importance to elements in it which remain unconscious."

COMPLEX, ANTI-OEDIPUS.—The attitude taken by an individual in order to overcome the Oedipus conflict.

COMPLEX, CASTRATION.—The ideas centered around the fear of losing the penis and the emotions linked with these ideas. The passive castration complex is the idea that the penis has already been lost and/or the wish to lose the penis.

COMPLEX, FEMININITY. Psychoanalysts believe that, in the infantile life of the boy, there is a phase equivalent to the 'penis' phase in the little girl. Girls believe that they once possessed a phallus just like the one that boys have but through some misdeed on their part it was taken from them. The male child develops the same fear of frustration (castration phantasy), which Klein calls a *feminity com-*

103

plex. In essence it is the inferiority complex of Adler. The boy thinks that the mother is the castrator. In order to save his phallus from the fate suffered by girls he identifies himself with his mother and wishes for a vagina and breasts. There is thus 'vaginal envy' in boys as there is 'penis envy' in girls. At the same time there is a dread on his part against the feminine role which castration would bring about. The dread may appear as its opposite, aggression. A tendency to excess in the direction of aggression which very frequently occurs has its source in the feminity-complex.

COMPLEX, INFERIORITY.—A common term in psychiatry. It refers in general to the existence of types of emotional adaptation that are of a lower order than is normally expected. It is characteristic of psychiatric states that they represent regressive forms of adjustment. For example, schizophrenia is a type of biological adaptation at some level below what is normally expected of the individual. The schizophrenic patient with a paranoid syndrome exhibits inferiority in his inability to grow up emotionally beyond the latency period, specifically beyond that of homosexuality. The catatonic and hebephrenic patients are inferior in the sense that they are instinctually fixated in the narcissistic and auto-erotic zones. The patient with conversion hysteria has never successfully handled the issues of the early Oedipus complex.

Psychiatrists have found that the instincts are subject to the general laws of growth that apply to organic matter. In general it may be stated that the Psyche, including, of course, its energic system, may lag behind in development, may progress normally or may advance too quickly. The indicated types of growth may involve the entire psyche, or any part of it.

Adler is known chiefly for the stress he places upon feelings of inferiority. He believes that everyone is born with an inferiority—organ or psychical—and that the manner in which the inferiority is handled determines the "style of life" led by the individual. He believes that psychiatric states are the result of faulty management of the inferiority characterizing the individual.

COMPLEX, MASCULINITY.—Rebellion against castration in the girl, leading to masculine attitudes and behavior. This term is used by Freudian psychoanalysts in much the same way that Adler uses masculine attitude in female neurotics.

COMPLEX, NOT-KNOWING.—The phrase *not-knowing* is sometimes referred to as a complex. A child's inferiority may be considerably re-enforced when he is led to believe that there are many things about which he should not know. When, for instance, adults carry on conversations with an air of secrecy and mystery, the child's curiosity impulse is aroused, but because it cannot know what the adults are talking about, it develops a "not-knowing" complex, the influences of which may modify the child's later personality growth to a great extent.

COMPLEX, OEDIPUS.—According to Greek mythology, Oedipus was a son of Laius, King of Thebes, and Jocasta, his wife. The King learned from an uncle that he was fated to be killed by his son. When a boy was born, the King gave him (with a spike driven through his feet) to a shepherd to leave him on Mt. Kithaeron to

104

die. However, the compassionate shepherd gave the infant to the childless King of Corinth, Polybus. When Oedipus reached the age of puberty and an oracle told him that he would kill his father and form an incestuous union with his mother, he decided not to return to Corinth to his alleged father. In his journey he met Laius, whom he slew in a quarrel. When Oedipus arrived at Thebes, the Sphinx presented a riddle for solution. Oedipus solved the riddle and the Thebans in gratitude gave him Jocasta as wife. When finally he discovered the relationship between him and his wife he blinded himself, while Jocasta hanged herself. Oedipus wandered away, accompanied by his daughter, Antigone, being finally destroyed by the avenging deities, the Eumenides. The principles of the Oedipus situation are regarded by psychoanalysts as characteristic of all individuals. Every child must pass through what is called the Oedipus situation or family romance. During the phase of late infancy, the child shifts a quantum of energy into sexual interests in the parents. Normally the boy becomes chiefly attached to his mother, the girl to her father. The solution of the struggle determines the character of the child's later reactions. During the latency period, the Oedipus complex is normally relinquished in favor of extraparental activities and interests. With the advent of puberty the original infantile Oedipus situation is again aroused, and is normally dissolved by the centering of interests in others.

However, the average psychiatric patient never successfully manages his Oedipus complex. The schizophrenic patient relives the Sophoclean tragedy often with minute precision, even to the point of claiming royal birth.

The same theme is common to psychoneurotic patients, but it is often highly symbolized as a fear, a compulsion, or a conversion phenomenon.

Freud is responsible for the introduction of the Oedipus concept into psychiatry. One says rightly that the Oedipus complex is the nuclear concept of the neuroses, that it represents the essential part in the content of the neuroses. It is the culminating point of infantile sexuality, which through its after-effects decisively influences the sexuality of the adult.

COMPULSION[1]–Action due to irresistible impulse. As a morbid phenomenon, it is an act contrary to the conscious will of the subject at the time the act is performed. When an individual carries out an act of which he is not conscious or aware, such as may occur during certain epileptic states or during a period of hysterical amnesia, the action is not known as a compulsion, for the action does not have simultaneous opposition from the subject. Nor is the term *compulsion* used in psychiatry to denote morbid action that has the approval and encouragement of the subject. This delimitation of the meaning of the term expresses the general opinion of psychiatrists today.

Compulsions are usually the result of obsessions. They are obsessions in action.

CONFABULATION.—In psychiatry, the act of replacing memory loss by phantasy or by reality that is not true for the occasion. The

1/Cf. with discussion of compulsion and obsession in main body, Chapter 3, Page 42

105

term implies also lack of insight, in the sense that the subject fully believes his answers to be correct. Confabulation is not uncommon in organic brain diseases in which intellectual impairment is a prominent feature. For example, the patient with a Korsakoff syndrome often fills in the memory gaps with incorrect details. A patient, bedridden in the hospital for months, said that he had just returned from a European journey and gave many details of the trip, believing thoroughly in his account.

Confabulation is to be differentiated from *pseudologia fantastica*, which occurs mainly in the 'psychopathic' group and in other conditions in which acting-out is prominent. In pseudologia fantastica, the phantasy is believed only momentarily and will quickly be dropped if the patient is confronted with contradictory evidence. The confabulator, in contrast, will stick steadfastly to his story.

COUNTER-TRANSFERENCE.—Annie Reich defines counter-transference as the effects on his understanding or technique of the analyst's unconscious needs and conflicts. The patient's personality, or the material he produces, or the analytic situation as such represents an object from the analyst's past, onto which past feelings and wishes are projected. A broader definition would include not only situations in which the patient serves as a real object onto whom something is transferred, but also those where the patient serves merely as a tool to gratify some need of the analyst, such as alleviation of anxiety or mastery of guilt feelings. Counter-transference is a necessary part of psychoanalytic therapy, for it is within the framework of counter-transference that the analyst's unconscious perception and understanding of his patient's productions come about, typically by means of partial and short-lived identifications with the patient at which points the analyst gains insight and comprehension of the patient's previously incomprehensible and confusing productions. But the analyst must be able to give up this identification and swing back into his objective role, thus preserving the neutrality of his reactions to the patient's emotions which makes the patient's transference possible.

Ideally, the analyst's unconscious mechanisms will be sublimated successfully into the qualities necessary for the practice of psychoanalytic technique. If this has not occurred, however, there may appear various undesirable counter-transference manifestations. These may be acute, temporary, and short-lived, and such manifestations are often based on identification with the patient or on reactions to the specific content of the patient's productions.

DEFENSE.—A mental attribute or mechanism or dynamism, which serves to protect the individual against danger arising from his impulses or affects.

The ego arises in response to the frustrations and demands of reality on the organism; it learns to follow the reality principle. But the id follows the pleasure principle only, so that often there are conflicts between the two. This is the essential neurotic conflict. The superego may take either side, and if the world and external reality appear to the ego to be sources of temptation, the conflict may appear to be between the world and the ego. The mechanisms of defense are developed as a means of controlling or holding in check the impulses or affects which might occasion such conflicts. The various motives for the development of defense-mechanisms are: (a) anxiety, arising when the ego believes the instinct is dangerous; (b) guilt, with anxiety of the ego toward the superego and fear of annihilation or decrease of narcissistic supplies; (c) disgust, when the ego must reject the impulse or it will have to be vomited out, and (d) shame, a fear of being looked at and despised if the impulse is not rejected.

Various defense-mechanisms have been described. L. E. Hensie lists 16 mental mechanisms: repression, reaction-formation, isolation, undoing, projection, introjection, identification, sublimation, displacement, condensation, rationalization, transference, symbolization and transposition, conversion, phantasy, and day-dreaming.

EGO.—In psychoanalytic psychology, the ego is that part of the psychic apparatus which is the mediator between the individual and reality. Its prime function is the perception of reality and adaptation to it. The ego is the executive organ of the reality principle and is ruled by the secondary process. The various tasks of the ego include: perception; motor control (action); adaptation to reality; use of the reality principle and the mechanism of anxiety to ensure safety and self-preservation; replacement of the primary process of the id by the secondary process; memory; affects; thinking; and a general synthetic function manifested in assimilation of external and internal elements, in reconciling conflicting ideas, in uniting contrasts, and in activating mental creativity. Unlike the id, the ego has an organization (i.e. it is not chaotic), it can generate co-ordinated action, and it is ruled by the secondary rather than the primary process. Its functions develop gradually, dependent upon physical maturation (and particularly, the genetically determined growth of the central nervous system) and upon experiential factors.

Beginning at birth, stimuli from the external world act upon the organism; over the ensuing months and years, with the accumulation of more and more experiences, certain mental events have a peculiar intimacy and a new psychic structure, the ego, is formed. The ego mediates between the individual and reality; it is a clearing-house for stimuli from both the unconscious and from conscious reality. It develops on the basis of unsatisfied instinctual demands (thus, if there were always to be satisfaction, there would be no development of reality).

The first fear is of a recurrence of the primal anxiety, and from this develops the fear that the child's own instinctual demands, which gave rise to the overwhelming excitation beyond his capacity to master, are dangerous in themselves. This fear is complicated by animistic thinking (the belief that the external environment has the same instincts as the self), for if the desire to recapture the primary narcissism is to be achieved by eating the parents, the child feels that the deed will be undone by his being devoured himself (talion principle). This is how anxieties of physical destruction originate; the most important representative of this group is castration anxiety.

The development of speech initiates a further decisive step in the development of reality testing, for tying up words and ideas makes proper thinking possible. Thinking is an anticipatory acting out done with reduced energy. The faculty of speech changes archaic, prelogical thinking ('primary process') into logical and orderly ('secondary process') thinking. With the arrival of speech and logical thinking, a final differentiation of conscious and unconscious is made. Now prelogical thinking will be used as a substitute for logical thinking only when the latter cannot master unpleasant reality.

The maturing ego must not only postpone action, but on occasion it must inhibit action completely. Thus the ego develops reactions of defense against instinctual impulses and turns against its own instinctual demands (countercathexis). There are various reasons for the development of these defenses: (1) instinctual demands that cannot be satisfied become traumatic in themselves; (2) prohibitions from the outside world, through education, experience, etc.; (3) the danger is phantasied because of a projective misunderstanding of the world; (4) the ego becomes dependent upon the superego (which has meanwhile developed), and anxiety is transformed into guilt.

EMOTION.—Agitated strong feeling. The most commonly accepted definition of emotion today includes reactions of an instinctive character that have both physical and psychical manifestations. 'It is surely of the essence of an emotion that we should feel it, i.e., that it should enter consciousness.' Freud maintains that the true aim of repression is to suppress the development of emotion, that is, to keep the emotion in the unconscious sphere. This means also that the ideas associated with the emotion are repressed. Apparently when both ideas and their associated emotions are relegated to the unconscious, the ideas continue 'as an actual formation' therein, but the emotion exists only as 'a potential disposition. Hence, there are no unconscious affects in the sense in which there are unconscious ideas. . . . The whole difference arises from the fact that ideas are cathexes—ultimately of memory-traces—whilst affects and emotions correspond with processes of discharge, the final expression of which is expressed as feeling.'

Emotional expressions are objective phenomena which may qualify instinctive behavior or betray an attitude. They consist of gestures, postures, movements of parts of the face, vocal expressions, modulations of the voice and many visceral changes.

EMOTION, CONVERSION OF.—The psychosomatic process through which an unconscious emotional conflict concerning the function of one organ is displaced upon and expressed, vicariously, through the energizing of the functional disturbance of another organ. In this process symbolic representation of organ function plays a major role.

Blushing is a good example of the displacement of the erotic functions of congestion, tumescence, and erection from their primary phallic (clitoral or penile) glans, or head, onto the head (caput) of the body as a whole. In this process the body, as a whole, functions symbolically and unconsciously as a phallus, and is utilized to express and carry out conflicts that relate primarily to the genital area, and not primarily to the organ involved.

EMOTION, SOURCES OF.—A psychoanalytic term that is particularly used and useful in emphasizing the root origins, in the unconscious, of the personal shibboleths and prejudices of so-called 'normal' individuals. This is especially important for those with pretensions toward objective scientific observations and judgments. By working through the defensive resistances rooted in the character, a degree of self-knowledge is achieved, which is, in a way, the ideal goal of the personal analysis. Through this process the emotional sources of rationalizations, self-delusions, self-deceptions, and confused obstructions to lucidity and clear understanding are uncovered. It is only through the intimate knowledge of one's own unconscious life that the emotional sources of bias and prejudice can be recognized and overcome.

ETIOLOGY.—The division of medical science relating to the cause of disease. The cause of general paresis is the germ of syphilis; not all patients with syphilis develop general paresis. Etiological studies involve also investigations into the nature and response of the tissues of the host as well as of the response of the total personality to the results of the disease.

FREE ASSOCIATION.—The trends of thought or chains of ideas which spontaneously arise when restraint and censorship upon logical thinking are removed and the individual orally reports everything that passes through his mind. This fundamental technique of modern psychoanalysis assumes that, when relieved of the necessity of logical thinking and, reporting verbally everything going through his mind, the individual will bring forward basic psychic material and thus make it available to analytical interpretation. 'Mistakes of everyday life, and dreams in which the partial liberation from fetters of logic and repression is already achieved, constitute a particularly interesting material in this respect.' This method was originally introduced by Freud after he had been disillusioned with the results of hypnosis. In trying to overcome the post-hypnotic amnesia, Freud found out that, when urged to make an effort, the hypnotized individual was able to recall almost everything that had been said to him, although he could not remember anything that had happened during the hypnotic trance.

Freud applied the same technique to patients he could not hypnotize. He 'urged them to tell him everything that came to their minds, to leave out nothing, regardless of whether they considered it relevant or not. He persuaded them to give up all conscious reflection, abandon themselves to calm concentration, follow their spontaneous mental occurrences, and impart everything to him. In this way he finally obtained those free associations which lead to the origin of the symptoms. As he developed this method, he found that it was not as simple as he had thought, that these so-called free associations were really not free, but were determined by unconscious material which had to be analyzed and interpreted. He, therefore, designated this new technique psycho-analysis.'

The combined work of repressive influences of the ego prevents the unconscious material from entering into the field of consciousness. Such material can be obtained only through the technique of free association. In other words, free association overcomes, or sidetracks, the repressive forces and makes it possible for the psychic unconscious material to come forward into consciousness. In this manner the psychiatrist is able to reach the inner layers of the mental life of the patient, interpret them, and finally bring them into the range of the patient's sight. The methodological principle of free association is a common basis for the classical Freudian analysis and the Jungian **type** of analysis.

FUGUE.—In psychiatry today, this term means a flight, so to speak, from reality in the sense that the individual becomes more or less completely unmindful of his environment and often of himself. He enters into a phase of so-called psychological amnesia, in which he may frequently seem to possess all his mental faculties, but questioning may reveal complete or partial amnesia for certain experiences.

FUNCTIONAL.—Relating to performance or execution. The heart has structure; when the structure works it is functioning; the psyche has structure; when the psychic structure works it is functioning. According to the most acceptable doctrines to day, the psyche is an organ of the body, intimately associated and correlated, as are the physical organs, with other bodily structures. Each organ has its own special constitution or organization, designed to operate in its own way and to produce particular end-results.

Nowadays, psychiatric states are sometimes referred to as 'functional disorders'; the expression meets the requirements of current psychiatric knowledge when it means what it says, namely, that the psychiatric condition observed is a manifestation of disordered function of the psyche, a disorder from a somatic standpoint, that is, instigated from the soma, or from a psychic point of view. The heart may show abnormal functioning, not because of any pathology of the heart, but because of some abnormal stimulation from a distant source. An analogous situation prevails with respect to the psyche. Or the functioning of the heart may be disturbed because of something unusual about the heart itself. Again, the psyche may exhibit an analogous condition.

HYSTERIA.—Unless modified by the word *anxiety* (i.e., anxiety-hysteria), the word hysteria usually refers to conversion hysteria. Clinically, the characteristic features of hysteria are: (1) a physical manifestation without structural lesion; (2) a calm mental attitude (called 'la belle indifference' by Janet); and (3) episodic mental states, in which a limited but homogeneous group of functions occupies the field or consciousness, often to the complete exclusion of the usual contents of consciousness—fugues, somnambulisms, dream-states, hypnotic states, etc. There is, in other words, a dissociation of the mental or bodily functions, and the dissociated function may operate in co-existence with normal consciousness, or it may operate to the exclusion of the other functions. In hysteria, the split-off function is ordinarily a unity and the splitting is seldom into more than two parts; thus it is commonly said that in schizophrenia the splitting is molecular or fragmentary, while in hysteria it is molar or massive.

There are no physical symptoms in hysteria that cannot be produced by volition or by emotion, although it may ordinarily be possible to maintain these symptoms for only a short time. Further, the physical symptoms correspond strikingly with the usual lay concepts of disease. Thus hysterical paralysis shows an exact delimitation and an excessive intensity, and it is more frequently accompanied by sensory disturbances than organic paralysis.

The *motor symptoms* include paralysis with or without contracture, tics, tremors, etc. The *sensory symptoms* include anesthesiae, paresthesiae, and hyperesthesiae; their distribution is rarely according to anatomical lines; they vary at different examinations; and they are susceptible to suggestions. Blindness and deafness are also seen. The *visceral symptoms* include anorexia, bulimia, vomiting, hiccough or respiratory tic, various abdominal complaints, flatulence, etc.

The *mental symptoms* include amnesiae, somnambulisms, fugues, trances, dream-states, hysterical 'fits' or 'attacks,' etc.

ID.—The id, as a psychoanalytic formulation, is part of the energy system of the psyche. It is regarded as the reservoir of psychic energy or libido; it contains all phylogenetic acquisitions and is the source of instinctive energy. The pleasure-principle reigns supreme in it and has control over the erotic and thanatotic (death) instincts. The id resides in the unconscious, far removed from reality, to which the id pays no attention. The id recognizes only its own needs and does not itself undertake to modify its needs in any way. Modifications of id impulses are brought about through other agencies, the superego and ego.

It is the obscure inaccessible part of our personality; the little we know about it we have learned from the study of dreamwork and the formation of neurotic symptoms, and most of that is of a negative character, and can only be described as being all that the ego is not. We can come nearer to the id with images, and call it chaos, a cauldron of seething excitement. We suppose that it is somewhere in direct contact with somatic processes, and takes over from them instinctual needs and gives them mental expression, but we cannot say in what substratum this contact is made. These instincts fill it with energy, but it has no organization and no unified will, only an impulsion to obtain satisfaction for the instinctual needs, in accordance with the pleasure-principle. The id knows no laws of logic; it knows no negation; it is timeless; it is 'virtually immortal'; it knows no good and evil, no morality. Instinctual cathexes seeking discharge, that is all that the id contains.

INSECURITY.—Insecurity, more commonly, emotional insecurity, is a feeling of unprotectedness and helplessness against manifold anxieties arising from a sort of all-encompassing uncertainty about oneself: uncertainty regarding one's goals and ideals, one's abilities, one's relations to others, and the attitude one should take toward them. The insecure person does not or dares not have friendly feelings in what seems to him an unfriendly world. He lives in an atmosphere of anticipated disapproval. He has no confidence today in yesterday's belief, no faith tomorrow in today's truth.

Almost without exception, the emotionally insecure adult was an emotionally insecure child. For it is in early childhood, in the home, that the foundations for the development of a secure personality must be laid. If this most important aspect of growth is neglected, the usual result is that the child will be seriously handicapped, probably throughout his life. For the emotionally insecure person there can be no effective living, no real happiness. The development of emotional security in the child is dependent upon the gratification of three specific needs: according to Preston's formulation, security rests on the three pillars of affection, approval, and consistency.

Genuine parental *affection* is as much a fundamental prerequisite

111

of wholesome development as is the need for food and shelter. Personality development is governed basically by the amount, genuineness, and kind of affection which an infant receives. Its presence or absence spells the difference between security and insecurity. There are no substitutes for affection.

Affection includes full *acceptance.* An affectionate parent accepts the child ror what he *is,* regardless of whether or not he approves of any one particular thing he *does.*

Children are unable to form the certainties which arise from *consistent* patterns, if they experience unpredictable fluctuations in which there is no cohesion. Frequent changes of residence and schools break constantly into any attempt at forming friendships, belonging to a neighborhood group, cementing the concept of "home," getting acustomed to a method of instruction. The child's need of consistency rests chiefly for its gratification on parental attitudes and parental behavior.

INSIGHT.—In psychiatry this term means the patient's knowledge that the symptoms of his illness are recognized as abnormalities or morbid phenomena. For example, when a patient who fears crowds realizes that the fear is a symptom of abnormality within his own mind but is unfounded in reality, he is said to have insight. When, on the other hand, a patient affirms that his body is composed of many other human beings, that God, Napoleon, Mithras, and others are actually within his organs, he is described as having no insight.

Insight is further defined from the standpoint of knowledge of the factors operating to produce the symptoms. When a patient says he understands the explanation regarding the origin and development of his symptoms, it is said that he possesses insight.

With perfect insight there is recognition of the abnormality through which the patient has passed.

INSTINCT.—Unreasoning impulse. In modern psychiatry the most commonly accepted concept of instinct is derived from the psychoanalysis of Freud. From the generic point of view it is usually agreed that an instinct is 'an organized and relatively complex mode of response, characteristic of a given species, that has been phylogenetically adapted to a specific type of environmental situation.'

McDougall says: 'Every instinctive process has the three aspects of all mental processes, the cognitive, the affective, and the conative. Now, the innate psychophysical disposition, which is an instinct, may be regarded as consisting of three corresponding parts, an afferent, a central, and a motor or efferent part, whose activities are the cognitive, the affective, and the conative features respectively of the total instinctive process.' McDougall says that the primary emotions, such as anger, fear, and disgust are instinctive, while what he calls secondary emotions, such as jealousy, hatred, and admiration, that is those compounded of two or more primary emotions, are not.

An instinct may be described as having a source, an object and an aim. The source is a state of excitation within the body, and its aim is to remove that excitation; in the course of its path from its source to the attainment of its aim the instinct becomes operative mentally. We picture it as a certain sum of energy forcing its way in a certain direction. See libido infra.

LIBIDO.—In the early years of psychoanalysis, when studies revolved principally around sexual issues, the energy associated with the issues was termed *libido*. As other concepts developed and the same instinctual forces were ascribed to them the expression *libido* was applied also to them.

Instincts are endowed with energy. The energy is called libido. From the psychoanalytic point of view it does not seem possible to separate the two, save in the sense that there are two fundamentally different kinds of instincts, the sexual or erotic and the aggressive or death instincts. It seems that the energy is the instinct.

MELANCHOLIA, MELANCHOLY.—A morbid mental state characterized by depression. It may be a manifestation of any one of a large variety of psychiatric nosologic states, although it is usually considered today as chiefly one of the phases of the manic-depressive psychosis.

The most ·exhaustive psychodynamic concepts on melancholia are derived from psychoanalysis. 'The distinguishing mental features of melancholia are a profoundly painful dejection, abrogation of interest in the outside world, loss of the capacity to love, inhibition of all activity, and a lowering of the self-regarding feelings to a degree that finds utterance in self-reproaches and self-revilings, and culminates in a delusional expectation of punishment. This picture becomes a little more intelligible when we consider that, with one exception, the same traits are met with in grief.'

NEUROLOGY.—The branch of medicine that devotes itself to the study of the organization and function of the nervous tissue. The diseases of the peripheral nerves of the spinal cord and the brain, as far as they are based on organic pathology, are in the realm of neurology.

NEUROSIS.—The distinctions between neurosis and psychosis are symptomatic, psychopathological, and therapeutic. In the neuroses, only a part of the personality is affected (Meyer's 'part-reaction'), and reality is not changed qualitatively although its value may be altered quantitatively (i.e. diminished). The neurotic acts as if reality had the same kind of meaning for him as the rest of the community. Psychopathologically, the psychotic change in reality is partly expressed as projection, and of a type which does not occur in the neuroses. In the neuroses, language is distorted and the unconscious may come to direct verbal expression. In the neuroses, the unconscious never attains more than symbolic expression, and regression to promitive levels (e.g., soiling and wetting) is not found in the presence of clear consciousness. Symptoms of neurosis include sensory, motor, or visceral disturbances and mental disturbances such as anxieties, specific fears and avoidances, memory disturbances, trance-states, somnambulisms, troublesome thoughts, and the like.

Charcot was the first to make a systematic study of the neuroses; he formulated a group of clinical pictures which he called hysteria, which was considered to be an outcome of hereditarily determined degeneration. Pierre Janet was the first to attempt a grouping of neuroses on the basis of their dynamics. He theorized that there are two kinds of psychological operations—easy ones, requiring the cooperation of only a few elements; and difficult ones, requiring the systematization of an infinite number of elements, involving a very new and intricate synthesis in each operation. When the 'nervous tension' or psychological force is lowered (by puberty, disease, fatigue, emotion, etc.) there is a general lowering of the mental level and only the simpler acts can be performed. Psychasthenia (including obsessions, compulsions, fears, and feelings of fatigue) results from a generalized lowering of the mental level; in hysteria, the lowering is localized in one particular function, which disappears (is dissociated) in consequence from the rest of the conscious personality.

General symptoms of the neurotic conflict include: (1) specific avoidances; (2) inhibitions of partial instincts (such as smoking and eating), of aggressiveness, of sexualized functions, and of emotions; (3) sexual disturbances such as impotence, premature ejaculation, and frigidity; (4) lack of interest in the environment and general impoverishment of the personality due to the constant drain of energy necessary to maintain counter-cathexes, and awarenesss of this impoverishment gives rise to inferiority feelings; (5) use of emergency discharges for the relief of tension, and (6) sleep disturbances, because of the many dreams and because of the fear of the ego to relax its guard during sleep.

NEUROSIS, ACTUAL.—In Freud's terminology, a true neurosis, i.e. symptoms which develop as a result of actual, true, or real disturbances of the sexual economy. Forced abstinence, frustrated sexual excitement, incomplete or interrupted coitus, sexual efforts which exceed the psychical capacity, sexual outlet rendered inadequate by guilt-feelings or other conflicts, the need to revert to more primitive and/or less satisfactory means of sexual expression—these are the common 'present-day' disturbances of sexuality which give rise to actual neurosis. Psychoneurosis, on the other hand, is determined by infantile and childhood experiences, and present-day occurrences are significant only in that they represent or repeat earlier events. Freud considered neurasthenia (a form of which is hypochondriasis) and anxiety-neurosis as true or actual neuroses.

NORM, PSYCHIC.—From the psychiatric point of view, a psychically normal person is one who is in harmony with himself and with his environment. He conforms with the cultural requirements or injunctions of his community. He may possess organic deviation or disease, but as long as this does not impair his reasoning, judgment, intellectual capacity and ability to make harmonious personal and social adaptation he may be regarded as physically sound or normal.

OBSESSION.[1]—An idea or an emotion (an impulse) that persists in the mind of an individual and cannot be gotten rid of by any conscious processes. From the standpoint of the conscious mind the obsession is uninfluenced by logic or reasoning and is distinctly unwanted.

Obsessions may be experienced by normal and abnormal individuals. An obsession may be regarded as normal when it does not interfere in any substantial way with the adequate performance of one's mental functions. This means that it is not long-lasting, that it only partially modifies sound thinking, and that its influence may be minimized or

1/Cf. with discussion of compulsion and obsession in main body, Chapter 3, Page 42.

114

nullified after a varying length of time by concentration of interests upon other topics.

Morbid obsessions are those that essentially control the conscious realm. They plague the individual more or less constantly, compelling him to act in such a way as to minimize their effects as much as possible.

PATHOLOGY.—The science of the nature of diseases.

PATHONEUROSIS.—Whenever there is an organic disease a varying quantum of emotions is directed to the sick organ or to a mental image of the sick organ as conceived by the patient. The well-adjusted individual gives adequate care (including emotions) to his illness, while he, who is so disposed, gives an inordinate quantity of feelings. An entire psychiatric syndrome may be invested in a sick organ. For example, the patient, with symptoms of appendicitis, may give expression to an underlying psychoneurosis, the type of psychoneurosis varying with the disposition of the individual. This condition is called pathoneurosis.

PSYCHE.—The psyche is the mind. In modern psychiatry the psyche is regarded in its own way as an 'organ' of the individual. The human organism is made up of a large number of organs or organic systems, such as the cardiovascular, neuromuscular, hepatic, nephritic, cerebral, endocrinal, etc. There is the 'organ' called the psyche which, like other organs, possesses its own form and function, its embryology, gross and microscopic anatomy, physiology, and pathology.

The most comprehensive schematization of the psyche is that drawn by Freud, consisting in general of the conscious and unconscious divisions, each of which is made up of a great number of components. The mind, like all other organs of the body has its own local functions and those functions that are intimately associated with adjacent and distant organs. It is like the cardiovascular system in that it reaches all parts of the body; it also serves to adjust the total organism to the needs or demands of the environment.

PSYCHEDELIC.—Mind-manifesting; sometimes used to describe certain pharmacologic agents which have an effect on mental processes.

PSYCHIATRY.—A branch of medicine that deals with the science and practice of treating mental, emotional or behavioral disorders, especially as originating in endogenous causes or resulting from faulty interpersonal relations. Webster's Unabridged Dictionary, 3rd ed.

PSYCHIC PRIMARY PROCESS.—A name given by Freud to the laws that govern unconscious processes. The intense forces operating in the unconscious or in the id are the organic instincts, which are continually striving for discharge, for satisfaction. This striving goes on according to what is known as the primary process, according to certain laws utterly different from those that have become familiar in conscious thought. An understanding of the primary process has been gained through the study of dreams, for in the formation of dreams instinctual impulses play the major role; they have forced themselves upon the ego and into consciousness. At the same time the unconscious material retains its own ways of working. The primary process can be observed at work in dreams.

The term primary process is used to refer to a type of thinking, characteristic of childhood, and/or to the way in which libidinal or

115

aggressive energy is mobilized and discharged. The basic characteristics of the primary process are a tendency to immediate discharge of drive energy (i.e. immediate gratification) and an extreme mobility of cathexis so that substitute methods of discharge can be achieved with relative ease. Primary process thinking is characterized by the absence of any negatives, conditionals, or other qualifying conjunctions; by the lack of any sense of time; and by the use of allusion, analogy, displacement, condensation, and symbolic representation. Drive energy characteristically remains unneutralized during the period of operation of the primary process.

In essence, the primary process is identical with Freud's formulation of the pleasure-principle. The difference between them is that while the pleasure principle is described in subjective terms, the primary process is described in objective terms.

PSYCHODYNAMIC.—The term psychodynamic relates to the forces of the mind. Ideas and impulses are charged with emotions, to which the general expression psychic energy is given. For example, delusions of persecution or obsessions or compulsions are described as psychodynamic phenomena, in that they are said to represent the results of activity of psychic forces.

PSYCHOLOGY.—The science which treats of the mind of man or other organism in any of its aspects; systematic knowledge and investigation of the phenomena of consciousness and behavior; the study of the organism and its activities considering it as an individual whole, especially in relation to its physical and social environment. Webster's Unabridged Dictionary, 2nd ed.

PSYCHOSIS.—In current psychiatry, mental disorder of a more or less special kind, which may or may not be associated with an organic disease. It is not considered in keeping with the available facts to refer to a psychosis as a disease, since the term disease is traditionally identified with pathology of tissues. For want of a better term psychiatrists speak of mental disorder when they refer to pathology of the psyche.

A psychosis is usually a severer type of mental disorder in the sense that all the forms of adaptation (e.g. social, intellectual, professional, religious, etc.) are disrupted. In order words, the disorganization of the personality is extensive.

PSYCHOSIS, FUNCTIONAL.—It is not clearly known today what the more intimate relations are between the soma and the psyche. When it is said that the heart possesses a functional disorder, it is usually meant that the cause is traceable as far as the heart; the source of disorder may be even more distant; likewise, when it is maintained that the psyche is functionally disturbed (as when we speak of a functional psychosis) the scope of the term functional is determined by our present state of knowledge. Thus, the best information we have today regarding, for instance, the psychoneuroses, carries us as far back as the psyche. Hence, a functional mental disorder is one which, insofar as knowledge permits, stems from the psyche.

A conservative description of *functional disorders* is given by William McDougall: 'There are two great classes of disorders of our mental life, those that are directly due to organic lesions of the nervous

116

system and those which seem to imply no such lesion, no gross injury to the structure of the brain, and which are therefore called "functional disorders." '

PSYCHOTHERAPY.—The art of treating mental diseases or disorders. Psychotherapy is a form of treatment for problems of an emotional nature in which a trained person deliberately establishes a professional relationship with a patient with the object of removing, modifying or retarding existing symptoms, of mediating disturbed patterns of behavior, and of promoting positive personality growth and development.

REPRESSION.—The concept is used extensively in psychiatry. The most exhaustive description of it was made by Freud. It may be briefly defined as the active process of keeping out and ejecting, banishing from consciousness, the ideas or impulses that are unacceptable to it.

When an instinct-presentation (i.e. an idea or group of ideas charged with affect) is painful to the contents of consciousness, an effort is made to thrust it into the sphere of the unconscious. It is possible to reduce to a minimum the influence of such an instinct-presentation by first breaking it up into its two basic components: the idea and the affective charge. This means that there are three things that are subject to repression: (1) the instinct-presentation; (2) the idea; (3) the affect. In many instances, when the entire instinct cannot be successfully repressed, either the ideational or the affective part may be. If the idea is repressed, the affect with which it was associated may be transferred to another idea (in consciousness) that has no apparent connection with the original idea. Or, if the affect is repressed, the idea, remaining, so to speak, alone in consciousness may be linked with a pleasant affect. Finally, if the whole instinct-presentation is repressed, it may at some later time return to consciousness in the form of a symbol.

For example, a son may consciously hate his father. The idea and the affect are repellent to him. He may repress both, but if the idea is strongly charged with affect, it strives to re-enter consciousness. It may return to consciousness in disguised form, for example, as hatred for some superior, unconnected with the father. If the idea alone of the father is repressed the hate may be transferred to someone else, who is not recognized by the individual as standing for the father. If the hate alone is repressed, the idea (father) may be cathected with love; in this last instance the hate may return to consciousness to be connected with someone not known to be a father-substitute.

RESISTANCE.—From the psychoanalytic point of view resistance is 'the instinctive opposition displayed towards any attempt to lay bare the unconscious; a manifestation of the repressing forces.

As you are aware, the whole of psychoanalytic theory is in fact built up on the perception of the resistance exerted by the patient when we try to make him conscious of his unconscious.

SCHIZOPHRENIA.—A term which Bleuler suggested as a replacement for the now generally obsolete term *dementia praecox*. By the term, Bleuler meant to designate what he considered to be one of the fundamental characteristics of patients so diagnosed, namely, the

117

splitting off of portions of the psyche, which portions may then dominate the psychic life of the individual for a time and lead an independent existence even though these may be contrary and contradictory to the personality as a whole. Bleuler rejected the term dementia praecox because in his experience profound deterioration (dementia) was not the inevitable end-result of the disease process, and because it did not always appear by the time of adolescence.

In 1911, Eugen Bleuler described the schizophrenias as a slowly progressive deterioration of the entire personality, which involves mainly the affective life, and expresses itself in disorders of feeling, thought and conduct, and a tendency to withdraw from reality. Bleuler noted that the schizophrenias were at times progressive, at times intermittent, and could stop or retrogress at any stage; but that they showed a tendency toward deterioration and, having once appeared, did not permit of a full *restitutio ad integrum*. Bleuler established the multidimensional nature of the schizophrenias and believed them to be organic; but at the same time, he stressed the interaction of psychogenic and physiogenic features in their psychopathology and development.

Bleuler subdivided the symptoms of the schizophrenias into two groups: (1) the fundamental, primary, or basic symptoms, which are characteristic and pathognomonic of the disease process; and (2) the accessory or secondary symptoms, which are often seen in the schizophrenias and which may even occupy the forefront of the symptom-picture, but which are seem in other nosological groups as well and particularly in the organic reaction types (acute and chronic brain syndromes). In this second group are included such symptoms as hallucinations, delusions, ideas of reference, memory disturbances (e.g. deja fait, deja vu), etc. The fundamental symptoms of the schizophrenias include: (1) disturbances in associations, (2) the disturbances of affect, (3) ambivalence of the affect, intellect, and/or will, (4) autism, (5) attention · defects, (6) disturbances of the will, (7) changes in 'the person', (8) schizophrenic dementia, and (9) disturbances of activity and behavior.

While the specific etiology remains unknown, mounting evidence favors the conception of the schizophrenias as a heredogenetic disease involving particularly certain enzyme systems of the body.

SOMA, SOMATIC.—The organic tissues of the body. Thus, the brain, heart, musculature, bone, constitute parts of the soma. Whether entirely correctly or not, the terms *soma* and *psyche* are often employed as if they were opposites. The psyche, however, is currently considered as an organ of the total individual; it is not looked upon as an antithesis of the soma, but rather as a harmonious constituent of the entire organism. See *psyche.*

SOMATOBIOLOGY.—The study of the biology of the body, as contrasted with psychobiology, which is the study of the biology of the mind.

SOMATOPSYCHIC.—Relating to or originating in both body and mind.

SYNDROME.—Group or set of concurrent symptoms which together are indicative of a disease.

SUPEREGO.—In psychoanalytic psychology, there are three functional divisions of the psyche: the id, the ego, and the superego. The superego is the last of these to be differentiated. It is the representative of society within the psyche (i.e. conscience or morality) and also includes the ideal aspirations (ego-ideal). The superego is mainly unconscious; its functions include: (1) approval or disapproval of the ego's actions, i.e. judgment that an act is 'right' or 'wrong'; (2) critical self-observation; (3) self-punishment; (4) demands that the ego repent or make reparation for wrongdoing; (5) self-love or self-esteem as the ego reward for having done right.

In general, the superego may be regarded as a split-off portion of the ego which arises on the basis of identification with certain aspects of the introjected parents. Since introjection and identification are among the earliest defense mechanisms to appear, it is obvious that the precursors of the superego are in evidence early in life, in the prephallic or preoedipal phase. Such precursors consist mainly of the various effects which the demands and prohibitions of the parents (and their surrogates) have on the child, and these are particularly evident in regard to bowel training (and thus Ferenczi's term, 'sphincter morality'). Yet until the oedipal phase, the superego does not make itself felt as a disturbance of the harmonious accord between the strivings of the ego and the strivings of the id. Morality in the young child, such as it is, is more a response to immediate external demands of the environment than obedience to an inner authority. It is only with the oedipal phase that the superego begins to take its final form as an internal authority which stands between ego and id, compelling pleasures, and imposing punishment (loss of self-esteem, guilt-feelings, etc.) for violations of its orders. The superego develops as a reaction to the Oedipus complex; as is often said, it is the heir of the Oedipus complex. It is a solution to the impulses of this period which have no prospect of succeeding in reality and which, if allowed to continue unchanged, would have been dangerous. These impulses, deriving from the id, are allowed access to the ego; the forbidden impulses (love for the mother, hatred of the father) are withdrawn from their objects and deposited in the ego, which thus becomes changed. The changed portion of the ego is the superego, and it contains the sadism which was originally directed against the father; so also does it contain the love originally felt for the mother, but the very process of introjecting the mother and changing the libido attached to the maternal object into ego libido has resulted in disexualization. Thus the love portion of the superego (the ego-ideal) is a non-sensual love.

What has happened, in short, is that the frustrations of the Oedipus complex have caused the ego to resort to primitive methods of defense; viz. introjection and identification. As a result, the oedipal objects are regressively replaced by identifications, and sexual longing for the maternal object has been replaced by an asexual alteration within the organization of the ego. These newly introjected objects, which replace the sexual and hostile impulses toward the parents, combine with the parental introjects from the prephallic period (internalized parental prohibitions), and the superego is formed.

THERAPY, THERAPEUTIC.—Treatment of disease. Pertaining to or consisting of medical treatment; healing, curative.

TRANSFERENCE.—In psychoanlytic therapy, the phenomenon of projection of feelings, thoughts, and wishes onto the analyst, who has come to represent an object from the patient's past. The analyst is reacted to as though he were someone from the patient's past; such reactions, while they may have been appropriate to the conditions that prevailed in the patient's previous life, are inappropriate and anachronistic when applied to an object (the analyst) in the present.

During psychoanalytic treatment, the repressed unconscious material is revived, and since this material contains many infantile elements, the infantile strivings are reactivated and seek gratification in the transference. As the most important relationship of the child is that with his parents, the relationship between patient and analyst established in the transference becomes analogous to, or, at times, even similar to the patient's relationship with his parents in childhood. The patient endows the analyst with the same magic powers and omniscience which, in childhood, he attributed to his parents. The traits of submissiveness and rebellion, in transference, likewise reflect the attitude of the child to his parents. The patient behaves irrationally in the psychoanalytic situation; it often takes a long time to make him see the irrationality of his behavior, which is deeply rooted in his unconscious infantile life.

Transference may be positive, as when the patient unrealistically overvalues or loves the analyst; or it may be negative, as when the patient dislikes or hates the analyst without due cause in reality.

It is to be noted that the term transference does not refer to reactions of the patient to the analyst that are based on reality factors in the therapeutic relationship; thus a patient may be angry with his therapist if the latter misses an appointment, but to call such a reaction a manifestation of transference is incorrect. It should also be recognized that transference can exist outside the analytic situation in relation to other people in the individual's environment.

120

INDEX

alcoholic disorders, intoxication   37, 90, 96
Adler, Alfred   13, 14, 17
annulment   96
anxiety   40, 42
arteriosclerosis   35, 36

blockage   10, G

character disorders cf. personality   44
chorea   38, G
collective unconscious   15
complex, inferiority
   inferiority   14, G
complex, Oedipus
   Oedipal   5, 6, G
compulsion
   cf. obsession   40, 42, G
Constitutional law   52, 54
constitutional rights   55
criminal intent   75, 85
criminal responsibility   86

defense   7, G
dementia   36, 45
determinism   5
divorce   95, 96,
Durham Case   86, 87
dynamic-cultural school   9

ego   6, 8, G
emergency admissions   61

encephalitis   36
epilepsy   35, 36
existential psychiatry   26
expert witness   73, 74
external world of reality   6

forensic psychiatry   4, 53, 73-76
free association   5, 10, 16, G
Freud   4, 5, 9, 10, 11, 13, 15, 16, 41, 44
Freudianism   5
Fromm, Eric   8, 9, 54

Horney, Karen   9-13, 44
hypnoanalgesia   23
hypnoanalysis, hypnosis, hypnotism   20-25, 92
hypnodontics   22
hypochondria   40
hypothetical question   74
hysteria   41, G

incompetent   55, 56, 57-72, 77, 78
id   5, 8, G
insanity   1, 53, 75
instinctual reservoir   5
involutional psychosis   47

Jung, Carl Gustav   15, 17

law   2, 53, 74

manic-depressive psychosis 45
mental deficiency 39

M'Naghten Case 86, 87, 88
narcissism 11
negligence, contributory negligence 82
neurasthenia 40
neurology 2, 36, G
neuropsychiatric 36
neurosis, war 40, G
neurotic character 8

obsession cf. compulsion 40, 42, G
organismic psychotherapy 26

paranoia 46, 47
paresis 33
personalities, Rank's 17
personality disorders cf. character 48
phylobiology, phyloanalysis 26
phobia 40, 41
presenile psychoses 35
procedural law 52, 53, 55
psychiatry 2, 74, G
psychoanalysis 5, 26
psychobiology 25

psychodrama 27
psychoneurosis 40
psychopathic personality 48
psychosis 40, G
psychosomatic medicine 49, G

Rank, Otto 16
re-active depression 43
repression 5, G
resistance 7, 10, G

schizophrenia 38, 45, 46, G
senility 34
society 53, 54
sociology 53
statutory law 52
substantive law 52, 53, 55
Sullivan, Harry Stack 7, 9, 53
superego 6, 8, G
syphilis 33

therapies 27, 28, 29
transference 7, 10, G

unconscious 5

vascular diseases 36
void, voidable 77, 95

ADDENDUM
TO
INDEX

Alcoholic disorders   personality disorders, 37; intoxication, 90; as invalidating marriage, 96

Alfred Adler   13; work explained, 14; influence on Horney, 17

character disorders   intoxication and, 37; discussed, 44

chorea   Huntington's, 38; St. Vitus dance, 38; G

complex, Oedipus
    oedipal   one of the cornerstones of psychoanalysis, 3; resolution of, as giving rise to superego, 4

dementia   defined, 36; as former name of schizophrenia, 45

ego   Freud's definition, 6; Sullivan's definition, 8; G

forensic psychiatry   definition, 4; 53; discussion, 73-6

free association   part of Freud's psychoanalytic procedure, 5; Horney's approval, 10; not part of Jungian technique, 16; G

Freud   work on psychoanalysis, 4-5; his psychiatry according to Jones, 5; Horney's evaluation, 9-10; on narcissism, 11; and Adler, 13; and Jung, 15; and Rank, 16; on normal and neurotic fear, 41; 44

123

Fromm   psychoanalytic school and character types,
                         8-9; criticism of American culture, 54

Horney   discussion of theories and books, 9-13; and
                         Adler, 14; 44

hypnoanalysis
  hypnosis
    hypnotism   discussion, 20-25; diagnostic uses, 92

incompetent   interlocutory rights, 55; 56; home care, 57;
                         commitments, 58ff.; emergency admissions,
                         61; release, 65; perils of, 70; contracts, 77;
                         necessities, 78

id   Freud's definition, 5; Sullivan's definition,
                         8; G

insanity   definition, 1; law of, 53; issue of, 75

neurology   definition, 2; disorders, 36; G

psychoanalysis   definition, 5; and existentialism, 26

schizophrenia   defined, 45; 46; confused with Huntington's
                         chorea, 38, G

Sullivan, Harry S.   work, 7; part of dynamic-cultural school, 9;
                         connection with the economy, 53

superego   Freud's definition, 6
superego   Freud's definition, 6; Sullivan's definition,
                         8; and Oedipus complex, 4; G

therapies   group, 27; shock, drug, 28; miscellaneous
                         physical, 29

transference   Freud's theories, 7; Horney's theories, 10;
                         G